Depthfinders

A Guide to Finding & Catching More Fish

Wayne Heinz

Depthfinders

A Guide to Finding & Catching More Fish

Wayne Heinz

Frank Amato
Publications

All inquiries should be addressed to:
Frank Amato Publications, Inc.
P.O. Box 82112
Portland, Oregon 97282
(503) 653-8108
www.AmatoBooks.com

Cartoonists: Bill Voiland, Kelly Wrenchey

ISBN-13: 978-1-57188-521-0
UPC: 0-81127-00374-7
Printed in Singapore

10 9 8 7 6 5 4 3 2 1

Contents

Chapter 1

Read the Water

An Anglers' Guide to Relationships:

1. Find a woman who fishes.   *3. Find a woman with a sense of humor.*
2. Find a woman who cooks.   *4. Find a woman who's good in bed.*

Make sure these four women never meet.

O
ne would think that, unlike an angler seeking four ladies, or a lady seeking four men, most of us would want one depthsounder that does it all. In reality, depthsounders do only two things.

Echoes: How Long? How Strong?

First, the name game: depthsounder, depthfinder, fishfinder, bottomsounder, echolocator, fish flasher ... different words, same gadget. We'll call it a depthsounder.

A depthsounder discovers two things – distance and density. Think of a depthsounder as a very precise clock that also produces electricity. Think of a depthsounder's transducer as a combination loudspeaker and microphone.

Depthsounder sends electrical pulses to transducer (its speaker). This vibrates a crystal in the transducer. Just like the speaker in your radio, these vibrations become sound waves.

Fish on the scope.
Screen shot from Garmin Echo 500.

As sound waves flow through water, they bounce off anything more or less dense than water. Shrimp, air bubbles, sea bottom, some fish – all echo.

The transducer (now a microphone) typically spends 98% of its time listening for these echoes. Echoes distort the transducer crystal's shape and make it vibrate. These vibrations create electricity.

The strength of each echo determines the strength (voltage) of that electricity. The transducer then sends electricity to the depthsounder.

Sonar beam. *Furuno U.S.A*

This all occurs in microseconds. The depthsounder detects these voltage fluctuations from the transducer and asks two questions – How long did it take for each echo to return? How strong is each echo?

With this data, your depthsounder paints the bottom on your screen and, hopefully, fish in the water. There's the simple part.

Demystify Your Depthsounder

Surface scatter. False echoes. Sensitivity scale. Amplitude bar. These are the mysterious parts. Like learning French, learning the language of depthsounders takes some study.

SONAR: *SO*und *NA*vigation *R*anging. Sound travels about a mile per second in water. That's 4.5 times faster than in air.

Salmon swimming 50' (15 m) beneath your boat? You will see that fish on your screen in 1/100 of a second. Sonar – Ten times faster than you can blink!

Unlike light waves, sound waves flow mechanically. One molecule of water bumps against another … and another … and so on. Like ripples from a raindrop, sound waves flow outward from the transducer until they hit something and are reflected back. These reflections (echoes) become our window to the underwater world.

This Raymarine Dragonfly uses different frequencies on a split screen to show a sunken ship.

Tech Talk | Traveling At the Speed of Sound

Sonar has been around since 1918, so acoustic engineers know a lot about the behavior of sound in water. Sound travels about 4,840' per second in freshwater; about 5,120' per second in saltwater (1,500 m/s; 1,545 m/s). These are average figures for the upper 2,000' of water, at 65 degrees. Sound travels a bit faster in warmer water and in deeper, denser water.

In the near-shore waters we anglers cruise, this slight speed difference makes no difference in our depthsounder's accuracy. Saltwater does make a difference in our depthsounder's performance. Sonar penetrates 25% to 50% less deep in saltwater. Why? The salt gets in the way.

Pebbles and Ripples

Frequency: the number of vibrations per second in the transducer's crystal. As frequency increases, wave length decreases.

High frequency: Drop a pebble in the water. Small waves ripple out, but not far. The ripples might bounce back from a water beetle. Those ripples probably never make it to the shore.

Low frequency: Drop a boulder in the water. Big waves, spaced far apart, roll across the water a long way. A beetle just rides the swell, undetected by the waves. Only when the waves hit a ship or shore, do they bounce back strong.

Sound waves of different frequencies work in the water column the same way as the pebble and rock waves work on the water surface.

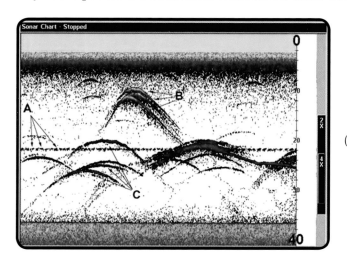

This Lowrance HDS 12 screen shows fish arches (B, C) in a thermocline (A).

Screen courtesy of Lowrance

Tech Talk | Crystals and Waves

Catalogs advertise the frequency of each depthsounder. "This model shoots deep, with its 50 kHz beam." A crystal's shape, thickness, and chemical formula determine the frequency of a sonar beam and its cone angle.

We measure frequency in Hertz. A Hertz is one cycle per second – one vibration of the sound-producing crystal in the transducer. A 200 kHz (200 kiloHertz) signal sends 200,000 sound waves through the water each second.

Like a fiddle that's not in tune, a depthsounder may play off-key, too. An individual 200 kHz depthsounder may send out signals at some frequency between 180 kHz and 220 kHz.

Although technicians cannot adjust the frequency of the transducer on your boat, they can tune a depthsounder to match the frequency of its transducer.

Expensive depthsounders – the $15,000 models commercial fishermen use – do just that. They tune in to the exact frequency of the signal. This optimizes echoes. Some of these commercial units monitor several different transducers. Other units monitor one transducer that contains up to 15 crystals. Only very high-end sportfishing depthsounders do this.

When Sound Hits A Thermocline....

Thermocline: the vertical zone where water temperature rapidly drops. Echoes arise when sound waves hit density changes. Water density depends on water temperature. Colder equals denser (molecules are packed closer together).

When sound passes through warm surface water, then hits the thermocline's colder water, the sound echoes back to the transducer. The thermocline then appears as a blanket lying across the middle of your screen.

A thermocline usually looks flat, faint, thin, fuzzy, and consistent, right to left. Mid-winter it might be absent, or only a foot thick. Late in summer it might be many feet thick. On windy lakes, spring and fall turnover erase the thermocline. On a swift or rough river, a thermocline may never form.

In dirty water, a false thermocline may form where detritus sinks, then suspends. Like fog scatters a car's headlight beams back to the driver, detritus scatters sonar beams back to the transducer. A false thermocline often looks darker than a real thermocline.

An oxycline, when the oxygen content of the water rises rapidly, usually due to a quick temperature drop, produces a sonar echo similar to a thermocline.

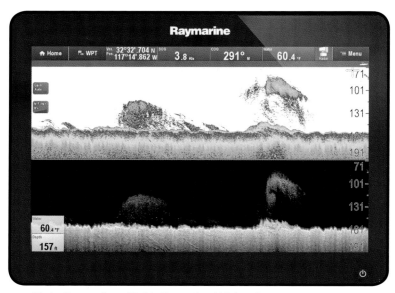

Find a thermocline with this Raymarine 165 that shows water temperature.

An ocean halocline, where salinity suddenly changes, produces a density change and will also echo.

Why do we look for a thermocline? With optimum temperature, sunlight, and nutrients, plankton thrive there. So baitfish dwell there. Where there's baitfish, there's....

Don't Let Jellyfish Fool You

During WW II, U.S. Navy sub-chasers were baffled by bottom readings several hundred feet deep ... in spots on the ocean several thousand feet deep. Worse, the bottom moved deeper by day, shallower by night.

Oceanographers figured it out. Sound waves were bouncing off dense swarms of jellyfish that migrated up and down the water column, following their food, plankton. The plankton fed in rich surface water by night, then avoided UV light by sinking deep by day. Sound echoed off the jellyfishes' air sacs.

Scientists now call this false bottom the DSL, Deep Scattering Layer. It can occur from several hundred feet to several thousand feet deep. Shrimp, krill, squat lobsters, and shiner perch can produce a DSL echo. When the thermocline and DSL coincide, the false bottom looks even denser. Now that you know about it, this false bottom won't fool you.

Read the Water Column Like A Book

Deciphering sonar echoes is much like reading a kids' picture book, but less clear. Saltwater signals: Kelp appears as thick, wavy, vertical streaks on your screen. Shrimp look like a thousand dots.

This Murre creates a trail of air bubbles that will show up on a depthfinder screen as a slanted string of dots. *Photo by NOAA, U.S. Dept. Commerce*

Saltwater: That endless, horizontal streak on your screen, 200' to 400' deep (60 m to 120 m), could be a few acres of prawns, or squat lobsters (pink, thumbnail-sized crustaceans). These signals are weak, just dots. Squid reflect sound well, and may show up on your screen as small blips or fingernails.

If you see a series of thin, slanted lines on your screen and birds are working bait, suspect the birds. As murres and other diving birds swim underwater, their feathers compress. This drives air bubbles out, forming bubble lines behind the birds. Sonar echoes off the birds' bubbles.

Commercial fishermen learn the acoustic signatures of each critter. With experience, you will, too.

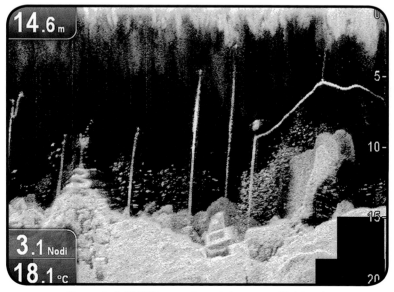

Raymarine's CHIRP sonar shows kelp on an artificial reef.

Cut Clutter

Like a smartphone downloading an app, a depthsounder gets a lot of data in a short time. The first data gives us the most trouble. The first dozen feet of water churns to froth from wave action and boat props. The froth's bubbles reflect sound waves. A layer of muddy water also reflects signals.

Result: clutter (often speckles) at the top of our screen. Combat clutter with the Surface Clarity Control (SCC) feature. Some manufacturers call this, Surface Turbulence Control (STC).

The factory sets the SCC/STC default at, "Off." In moderate seas, dial it up to "Medium." In heavy seas with breaking waves, dial it up to "High."

Other confusing echoes arise from algae and turbulence. Open water can get roily. A rip echo is the worst example of confusing echoes. Rip echoes are irregular and vary in strength. Looks like a mess on the screen. On a big, running tide, a rip may extend 80' down (24 m).

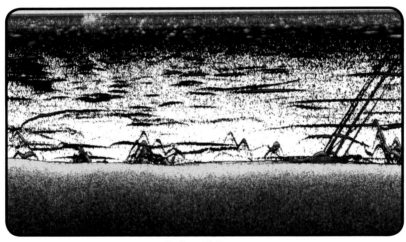

Surface Clutter
Purple haze, top = surface clutter
Diagonal lines at right = hooked fish, being reeled up

Set Up Your Depthsounder

You probably know anglers who turn their depthsounder on as they cast off from the dock ... and don't touch that depthsounder again until they tie up to the dock. What a waste of good sound waves!

View your depthsounder as a machine of many uses, a machine that needs adjusting as conditions dictate. Unless you own a unit that comes from the factory with pre-programmed settings (like Lowrance's "Fish

Clarify Your Screen: Switch to Manual Mode

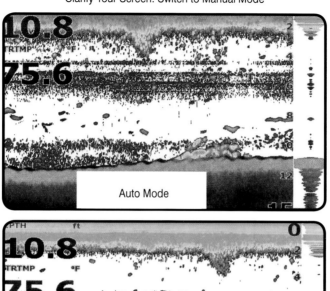

mode, Cruise mode, Troll mode...."), or a unit that allows you to pre-set your own, custom modes before you fish (like some Vexilar models), push plenty of buttons.

You can't hurt the depthsounder – no moving parts. Here are some common adjustments. Your depthsounder may require others.

- ✓ Choose a screen background
- ✓ Adjust brightness and contrast. Increase contrast for a sharper screen in bright sun.
- ✓ Fishing in low light, choose "Night" mode or "Backlight."
- ✓ Select "Auto" range mode, or "Bottom track" to continuously keep the bottom on the screen. "Auto" is the factory default.
- ✓ Set the range scale to "Manual" mode if you want to track a portion of the mid-water column.

✓   Set up the windows (full screen, split-screen, quad-screen...).

✓   Choose a fishing mode (troll, drift, anchor...) if available.

✓   Choose a sonar beam (down scan, side scan, look ahead...).

✓   Adjust gain, surface clutter control, and noise suppression.

✓   Set chart speed and ping speed.

✓   Set alarms (depth, fish, temperature).

✓   Choose data to overlay on the screen.

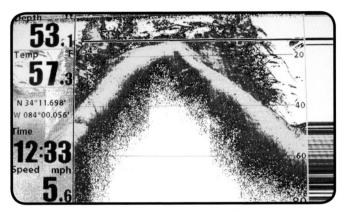

We can overlay data on Lowrance HDS screens.

Set Up the Transducer and Calibrate Depth

Depthsounders are set up at the factory to use the transducer included in the box. Bought a different transducer? Via an on-screen, compatibility menu, tell the depthsounder what transducer it will use, and the frequency.

Note: Screen frequency and transducer frequency must match. We can't marry a 50 kHz depthsounder to a 200 kHz transducer.

Calibrate Depth

The factory sets depth assuming the transducer sits at the water's surface. Your transducer may sit under the surface. You can calibrate it to read true depth. Manuals often call this feature, "Keel offset." To read true surface-to-bottom depths, add distance to the factory figure. To read depth beneath your keel, subtract distance.

Push the Buttons

Sounds like a lot of work, doesn't it? Half of these set-ups we only adjust at trip's start. Others, only when dark clouds blow in or we change our method of fishing.

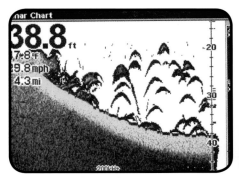

Fish on the scope.

Granted, you are on the water to fish, not fiddle with gadgets. But if you take the time to master your depthsounder's features, you'll fish more effectively.

We'll discuss all of these features in detail, chapter by chapter.

Remember: You can practice in your driveway in "Simulation" mode.

Ready to fish. Author at the helm.

Quick Tips	Read the Water

> ▸ *Take the time to set up your screen.*
> ▸ *Calibrate your screen's depth readout.*
> ▸ *Set the range scale to "Auto" mode, or "Bottom Track" to continuously paint the bottom on your screen. "Auto" is the factory default.*
> ▸ *Set the range scale to "Manual" mode if you want to track a portion of the mid-water column.*
> ▸ *Use SCC/STC to cut surface clutter.*
> ▸ *Use noise suppression sparingly.*
> ▸ *Discount signals from an ocean rip.*
> ▸ *Look for a thermocline – a faint, consistent, flat line.*
> ▸ *Look for an oxycline and a halocline.*
> ▸ *Birds diving on bait may appear as slanted lines (bubble trails).*
> ▸ *Weak dots deep may be shrimp or prawns.*
> ▸ *Jellyfish can produce a false bottom.*

Find More Fish

Things are getting curiouser and curiouser. —Alice

W hat quickens your pulse? "Fish on the screen," sounds nearly as good as, "Fish on!" right? But ... are those fingernails really fish? The more you stare at the screen, the more you mumble, like Alice in Wonderland, "Things are getting curiouser and curiouser."

Fingernails and Fish Bladders

"My depthsounder spots fish like magic!" Forgive this Angler in Wonderland his exuberance. Like a magician sweeps his hand behind your head and changes a nickel into a silver dollar, a transducer sweeps the water to produce blips that may not be as they seem.

What does a fish look like on our depthsounder screen? A fingernail ... sometimes. A half nail, a spike, a horizontal line, a blip ... sometimes. Big and dark, small and light ... sometimes. A fish mark is like the prize in a Cracker Jacks box: You never know what you're going to get!

Searching the ocean for fish, we face a problem: Fishes' bodies are about the same density as seawater. So sound waves pass through fish about the same as they pass through water. Scales, bones, and stomach contents of fish reflect sound waves poorly. Result: Weak echoes. Few fingernails. On lakes and rivers, same problem.

Photo by Lucie Fritz

Most freshwater gamefish, like this 18.6-pound Columbia River walleye, have an air bladder.

But fishes' air bladders – that's a different story! Big difference between the densities of air and water. Result: Air bladders produce strong echoes. Big marks on our screen.

Fortunately, most game fish, like bluefish, salmon, and bass, have air bladders. Unfortunately, some fish don't.

Deep-dwellers (like yelloweye) whose air bladders have shrunken; fish with vented air bladders (like lingcod, greenling, and cabezon); fast, offshore species with small air bladders (like tuna, mackerel, albacore); or fish lacking air bladders (like halibut, flounder, and sole) are harder to detect. Sharks, rays, and dogfish, with cartilage instead of bone, are also hard to detect.

Tech Talk | Fish and Frequencies

A sound wave at a low frequency of 50 kHz is about an inch long (2.5 cm). It will bounce off any fish whose air bladder exceeds an inch (2.5 cm) high.

A sound wave at a high frequency of 200 kHz is about 1/4 inch long (0.6 cm). It will bounce off any fish whose air bladder exceeds 1/4 inch (0.6 cm).

So the higher the frequency, the better the detail on your screen. Higher frequency also lessens background noise and works well at higher boat speeds.

But since water absorbs high-frequency signals faster than low-frequency signals, choose low frequency to find fish in deep water (200', 60 m).

A dual-frequency depthsounder with a split-screen provides a good way to compare frequencies. In less than 200' of water (60 m), with 50 kHz and 200 kHz pictures side by side, you'll notice the better detail in the 200 kHz window.

See More Fish

First, we aren't looking for a fish. Trying to find one fish is like going to an Easter Egg Hunt where they hid one egg. To have a reasonable chance of success, we're looking for a school of fish.

The school might be there. But are you seeing it? Try these tricks to paint better fish arches on your screen.

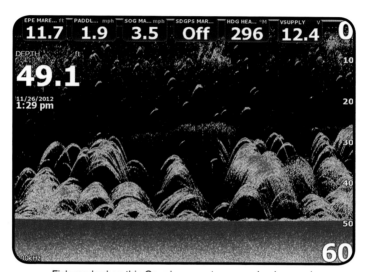

Fish marked on this Garmin screen's reverse background.

- Do you have a dual-frequency depthsounder? Do you usually fish in less than 200' of water (60 m)? Begin fishing with the high-frequency, narrow-cone option (usually 200 kHz) – good detail.
- Dual frequency: If no fish appear, switch to the low-frequency, wide-cone option (usually 50 kHz). Fish stay in the wide cone longer, so they echo better on your screen.
- Fishing early a.m. or late p.m., when gamefish might be near the surface? Switch to "Manual" mode. Set screen range to top 50' (15 m). Study only this upper zone.
- Does your depthsounder allow you to choose a screen background from a color palette? Reverse the screen background to see fish amid clutter.
- Avoid 3D mode for precise work. 3D averages depths, and misses fish. Use 3D to visualize bottom structure and search for fish shadows on the bottom. Then switch to regular 2D mode to spot fish near that structure.

Zoom   Just as your camera can zoom in on an eagle in the sky, your depthsounder can zoom in on a fish in the water. You already do this. But do you pan-zoom? To search for fish, slide the screen window through the water column (pan-zoom).

Zoom to track the bottom, magnify a fishy-looking zone in mid-water, or track your downrigger. When you zoom in, you put more of the screen's pixels in a smaller slice of water.

Example: If your depthsounder has 200 vertical pixels, and you're fishing in 200' of water, each pixel represents 1' of water. It would take a huge fish to create more than a single dot on your screen.

Zoom in to show just 50' (15 m) of the water column, and each pixel represents 3" of water (50' divided by 200 pixels = 0.25' of water = 3"). Now a fish will show up as many pixels. You can zoom in to see just the bottom 50', or any mid-water range. You can do this in full screen or split screen.

To find mid-water fish, switch from auto mode to manual mode. Set the vertical range narrow (top and bottom limits). Then zoom in. Result: Excellent target separation. Turn on your "Fish Track" feature or scroll your cursor to paint a depth number beside each fish arch.

Note: As zoom expands a target vertically, it compresses it horizontally. Result: a distorted screen image.

This Garmin Echo 550c zooms to spot fish better via split screen.

Sharpen Fish Arches

Fish arches are tricky. They depend on the depth of the fish, its position in the sonar beam, boat speed, fish speed, and the transducer's angle in the water.

Fish icons are even trickier. Humminbird calls their icons, "Fish ID." Furuno calls their fish size feature, "Accu-Fish." Both estimate the length of a fish by its echo. Hmmm.... Suggestion: Turn these "Fish ID" features off. Here's why.

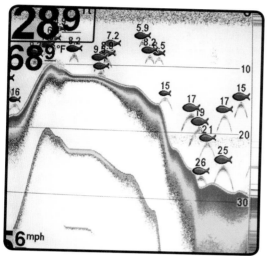

Fish ID icons tell us a fish's distance from the transducer, not how deep it swims.

A sound wave is blind. Like a soldier shooting at night, sound doesn't know what it hit. It doesn't recognize a turtle from a crab pot, from a seal, from a fish. Fish ID's software misidentifies junk as fish; fish as junk.

Arches show better detail than fish ID symbols. Exception: Some screens show fish arches, fish ID symbols, and fish depths all on the screen simultaneously.

Keep your boat moving. To paint good fish arches, either the boat or the fish must move. Here's why: As your boat moves forward, a fish ahead produces echoes closer and closer to the transducer. On your screen, the pixels rise. As your boat passes this fish, echoes come from farther and farther away. The pixels sink. Result: an arch.

Slow down. Remember: The transducer sends its signals out in the shape of an upside-down cone. Fish will remain in the sonar cone longer if you go slower. The arch will elongate. A fast boat compresses the echoes into a steeple or spike. The best fish arches occur at trolling speed.

Un-Arches Are OK

Shallow fish (closer than 30'; 9 m) seldom yield good arches. The sonar's cone is narrow near the boat. These fish are not in the cone long enough to produce many pixels.

See streaks on the screen? No, you do not have cataracts. When a fish quickly swims away from the boat, it produces a thin line. Although the line may descend on the screen, the fish may really be swimming horizontally. A descending line just shows the fish is moving farther away from the transducer.

Stationary fish under an anchored boat appear as a horizontal line. Only if the fish swims away, rises, or sinks in the water will the line slant.

Seeing mostly half-arches? That's normal. Fish on the edge of the cone produce pieces of arches, or narrow, pointed arches. Only centered fish produce round or flattened arches.

We see perfect arches mostly on simulated screens at sports shows. To get a perfect arch, a fish must pass through the center of the cone. Then it must exit the cone at the same level, 180 degrees from where it entered. Seldom happens.

Fish arches are created when the cone of sound passes over a fish. The distance to a fish when the cone first strikes it is shown as "A". When the center of the cone strikes the fish, the distance is shorter as shown "B". As the cone leaves the fish, the distance increases again as shown in "C".

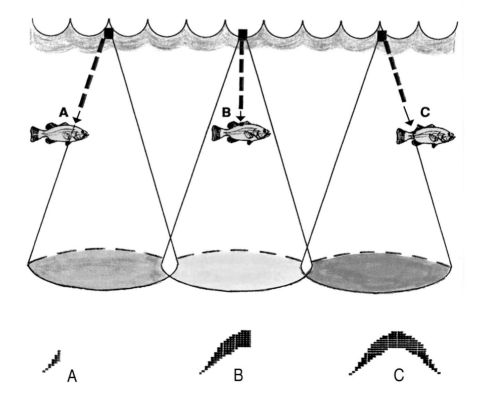

See More Fish — Turn "Fish I.D." Off

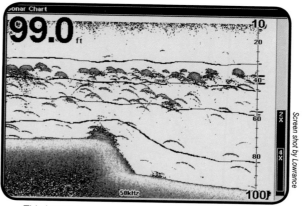

This Lowrance screen shows downrigger cannonballs.

In general, pivot the transducer to keep its face parallel to the water's surface. A transducer that tilts too far forward or backward produces poor arches. Mostly fragmented arches? If most half-arches slope up, but not back down, the front of the transducer might be too high. Tip the transducer's aft end up a bit.

If most half-arches slope down, the transducer's nose might be angled too far down. Tilt the transducer's aft end down a bit. Experiment with attack angles that show fish without messing up your screen.

Note: A depthsounder only paints fish that are closer to the transducer than the bottom is. If your boat is in 60' of water (18 m), with a fish 80' away (24 m), far to the side of the cone, it will not show, even though your transducer sees it. Exception: side-scan sonar.

Fish-Arch ID Key

Here are some ideas to help interpret your screen. Caveat: None of these ideas are foolproof.

- Full arch – Fish swims directly under the boat for a while.
- Half-arch – Fish swims on edge of cone.
- Fragment of an arch – Fish swims shallow or far to the side.
- Round or flat arch – Fish is centered in cone.
- Long arch – Fish stays in cone awhile.
- Steep arch – Fish was in the cone a short time.
- Pointed arch – Fish is on edge of cone.
- Slanted streak – Fish swam away fast.

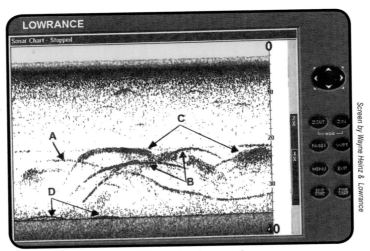

Is that fish swimming away?

Vary Chart Speed

The speed that a column of pixels crosses the screen varies from 1/50 inch per second to about ½ inch per second. The faster old data moves right to left, the quicker new data can show up. If the chart moves too slowly, data gets compressed and distorted. Fish arches become blobs, or mere points. We need about 1/10 inch per second to see good detail.

The factory usually sets chart speed at a default of 100%. That's OK. But sometimes we need to vary chart speed to best see fish. Although pushing buttons and hearing beeps is not why you are on the water, a minute or two of patience will put more fish on the scope.

Trolling? Leave chart speed at 100%. The faster the chart speed, the more pixels are turned on as the fish passes below. Data scrolls fast, right to left, spreading those pixels across the screen. You'll get good fish arches.

Cruising? Set chart speed slower. Produces average arches. Drift-fishing? Set at about 75%. Anchored? Try 50%. This will show fish below an anchored boat as short lines.

Stop the Screen

Many depthsounders allow us to stop the screen to study fish. "Stop" cuts off the flow of signals from the transducer. We can also review recent image history by temporarily scrolling the screen backward, left to right.

Most Furuno models let us view 15 minutes of history. Lowrance and Simrad call their history feature, "Trackback." Coupled with a GPS "quick-save" waypoint, trackback can put us back on the fish.

Haystacks and Comets

Baitfish often appear on our screen as a haystack. The denser the stack (lighter gray on a monochrome screen), the tighter the bait ball, the hotter the color. Orange/red inside a school of bait (light gray, on monochrome) means a densely packed school. Predators have balled up the bait.

Gamefish usually appear as red/orange arches beneath the haystack (black, on a monochrome screen). A light yellow haystack (loose, dark gray on monochrome) suggests less-panicked bait. Fish it anyway. You never know....

The Case of the Disappearing Salmon

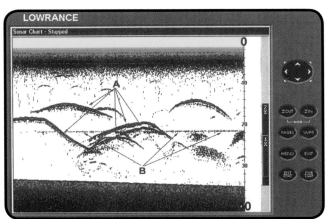

Here's what happens when you troll too close to a ball of herring: You scare your fish. The steep lines (A) trailing down to the right of the screen are salmon swimming away from your boat. Maybe they're swimming deeper: maybe just farther to the side. Either way they wont be flopping in your fish well. These fish are associated with a thermocline (B).

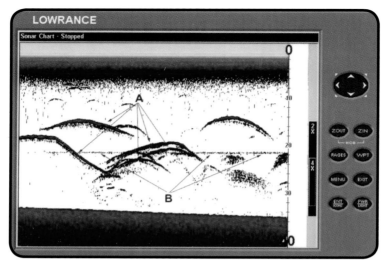

Fish Streaking

Faint, level line, center screen = thermocline (B). Fish (A) swim away from boat. This is an example of streaking. It occurs when your 'sounder begins to mark fish. Then the fish notice the boat shadow, motor noise, or other stimulus and swim rapidly away. Although the streaks go down, it doesn't necessarily mean the fish swam deeper, only that they moved further away from the transducer. They may have stayed at the same depth and simply showed their tails to the boat.

When bait appear on our screen as a comet, they're probably swimming to new water. Fish the tail of the comet. That's where gamefish pick off stragglers.

Baitfish that appear on our screen as scattered dots suggests that the bait is leisurely feeding on plankton. Gamefish may be around, but inactive. Troll a reaction-strike lure, like a bright spoon, through the deeper dots.

Own a fish flasher with a circular screen? Vexilar's flasher paints strong echoes red (nearest fish), average echoes orange (fish farther away), and weak signals green (fish farthest away). A series of lines close together, green/orange/red, could mean a fish is swimming closer to the transducer (into the sonar cone and more directly under the boat, where signals are stronger).

Target: a school of yellowfin tuna.

Photo by NOAA, U.S. Department of Commerce

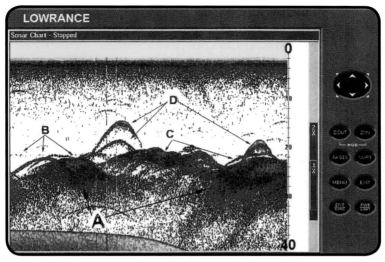

The Dream Screen: Bait & Salmon
A= Bait
B= Thermocline
C= Salmon feeding
D= Salmon less active

Quick Tips	Find More Fish

▸ *Choose a high-frequency sonar beam in shallow water.*
▸ *Choose a low-frequency sonar beam in deep water.*
▸ *Orient transducer face parallel to water surface.*
▸ *To see more fish, turn "Fish ID" and "3D" off.*
▸ *For better fish arches, keep your boat moving.*
▸ *A half-arch marks a fish that swam at the edge of the cone.*
▸ *Streaks on the screen are often fast-swimming fish.*
▸ *Turn "Fish alarm" on.*
▸ *Adjust screen brightness and contrast to see better detail.*
▸ *Set range to "Manual." Choose upper & lower limits to display only the zone you're fishing. Then zoom in.*
▸ *Set chart speed "Fast" for trolling; "Slow" for cruising.*
▸ *Search for baitfish before you look for gamefish.*
▸ *The hotter the color of the center of a bait ball, the denser the ball.*
▸ *Reverse screen background color to see fish amid clutter.*
▸ *Scroll back to study a past screen.*

Zero In

It's not what we don't know that hurts us. It's what we think we know … but ain't so … that gets us in trouble.

—Will Rogers

Despite today's advanced software, depthsounders do have limits. Staring at blips, we need to keep these limits in mind. Fish on the screen: Some things we can know about them. Some things we cannot know. Let's look at four fish data that are difficult to pin down.

How Deep Is That Fish?

Nobody knows. A depthsounder tells us how far away a fish swims, not how deep. If a salmon swims off the side of your boat, at the edge of the depthsounder's cone, 50' (15 m) from your transducer, your depthsounder will paint that fish as a blip, 50' (15 m), on your screen's vertical range scale.

But the salmon may be swimming only 24' deep (7 m) in the water column. The deeper you fish, the wider the cone, the greater the potential error. Side-scan sonar reduces this error, but does not eliminate it.

Example: Your guide stares at a down-scan screen and says, "There's a bass right next to a boulder, 75' under the boat (22.5 m). Drop your jig straight down." The boulder's there, sure. But is the bass? What if that bass is swimming way off to the left, 75' from the transducer (22.5 m), maybe 50' deep (18 m)? Where will the depthsounder paint that bass? Right beside that 75'-deep boulder (22.5 m).

This is bad news, I agree. Like a seven-year-old boy in December who's hearing dark rumors from his classmates, we want to believe in our depthsounder. After all, that bass might well be by the boulder. Then again...

Think Up-side-Down

Let's look at cone coverage at modest depths – less than 200' (60 m). If we assume that only 1/4 of the main area of the cone is directly under the boat, then 3/4 of the time the fish will be off to the side, and shallower than it shows on the screen.

When you scroll the depth cursor to the fish, always think 3-D. Picture an upside-down ice cream cone. Fish can be anywhere in that cone.

Get into the habit of reading the numbers on the vertical scale as, "distance away from the transducer." Say out loud, "Marking fish, 50' away." Think, "These fish are somewhere above 50'." Then you won't make the mistake of trolling your bait exactly 50' deep for 20 minutes without a strike (15 m).

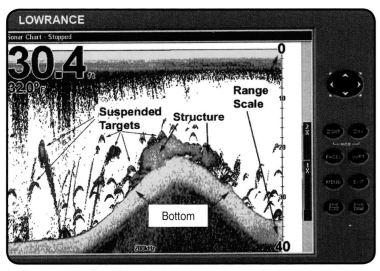

Read the vertical scale as range, not depth.

Tech Talk | Cone Angles

Cone angle: flashlight vs. floodlight. Like a flashlight beam, a narrow transducer cone shoots directly under the boat. But, like a floodlight, a wider cone finds more fish off to the side.

The transducer's crystal determines cone angle. Unlike some flashlights that allow us to change their beam angle, a transducer's cone angle is fixed.

A crystal that produces a narrow cone seems more powerful than one that produces a wide cone. Why? Because the narrow cone beams the power into a smaller area.

Note: Your transducer's actual cone coverage usually exceeds the coverage of the transducer's rated cone angle. Just as you can faintly see objects in the fringe of a flashlight beam, a 20-degree transducer may faintly detect objects out to 60 degrees. We call these, "side lobe images." Expensive transducers focus their energy in the main beam and minimize side-lobe energy.

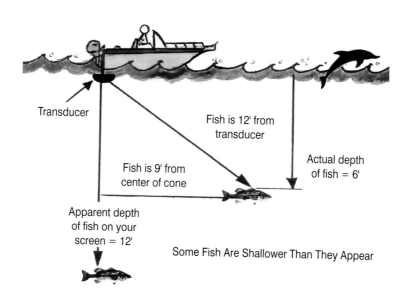

Some Fish Are Shallower Than They Appear

The 20-degree cone rating just means that half the transducer's power is concentrated in an arc of 20 degrees. Outside that arc, the remaining power weakens rapidly, but still pings things. To widen the effective cone coverage, turn the gain (sensitivity to echoes) up. You'll see fish farther to the sides.

We can buy depthsounders with cone angles rated 7 degrees to 200 degrees. Mid-range cone angles – 20 degrees to 60 degrees – are most common. Most manufacturers offer a choice of several cone angles for a given frequency. We can buy 200 kHz Humminbird transducers with cone angles of 60, 45, 34, or 20 degrees. Our choice depends on the depth we usually fish and the side-scan we want.

Low-end depthsounders shoot one cone angle. More expensive, dual-frequency depthsounders offer two different cones from two crystals in the same transducer. Vexilar offers a tri-frequency transducer. Humminbird offers a quad-beam transducer.

Shortcut for Cone Coverage

Jot down the cone angle of your depthsounder at each frequency and keep your notes at the helm.

Here's a quick way to estimate how wide your main sonar beam is at any depth.

Cone angle, in degrees:	60	45	30	20	10
Cone diameter:	same as depth	3/4 of depth	1/2 of depth	1/3 of depth	1/6 of depth

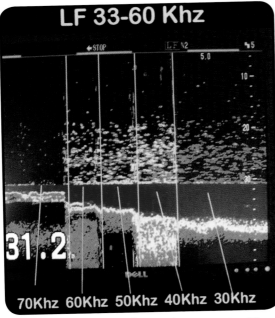

LF 33-60 Khz

70Khz 60Khz 50Khz 40Khz 30Khz

Fish images at different frequencies. *Image courtesy of Airmar.*

Example: A 20-degree cone covers a circle about 1/3 the depth of the sonar beam. Bottom 90' deep? Cone's diameter there is about 30'.

Another quick estimate: Find cone coverage (diameter) at *FurunoUSA.com/ LearningCenter/Transducer-Beam-Angle-Calculator.* Enter cone angle and target depth. Click on, "Calculate."

Double Your Odds

Own a dual-frequency depthsounder? Scan for fish with the wide-angle cone (lower frequency). Then zoom in with the narrow angle cone (higher frequency) to more accurately judge the fish's depth.

Let's say you're drifting slowly. A fish, let's say a lake trout, shows in the wide-angle cone. But it disappears when you switch to the narrow-angle cone. That laker swims way off to the side of your boat, right? That's why it disappeared when you narrowed the cone. The laker swims shallower than it appears on your screen.

If you are cruising at high speed, this trick won't work. The laker will disappear anyway. The cone quickly passes it by.

Trolling with a downrigger? Cable angle about 45 degrees? A wide-angle cone picks up deep cannonballs better. If you have dual frequency/split screen, keep the high-frequency, narrow-cone beam in one window to better define fish.

Where's That Fish?

Hide 'n seek is easy compared to figuring out where a fish glides beneath our boat. We do have some tricks to ease the task, though.

Sound waves are concentrated and strong in the center of the sonar cone. They are diffuse and weak at the edges of the cone. To see if a school of fish is centered beneath your boat, slowly turn your depthsounder's gain down.

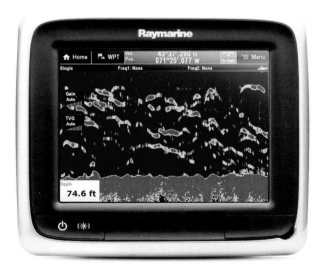

This Raymarine a67 with CHIRP, shows fish all through the sonar beam.

If the fish are centered, they will stay on your screen. The power in the center of the beam will continue to paint their arches well. The better the arch, the more likely the fish are really at the depth your screen says they are.

If the fish are near the edge of the cone they will fade from your screen. Again, we can guess these fish are shallower than their screen depth.

The wider the cone angle, the more likely a fish will appear deeper than it really is. You can prove this if your depthsounder displays a split-screen (200 kHz/50 kHz). Why do we talk about these depth delusions? So you won't commit a cardinal angling sin – fishing under the fish.

Most gamefishes' eyes sit high on the sides of their heads. These predators search for baitfish silhouetted against the sky. Example: Silver salmon look up. Silvers look to the sides. Silvers seldom look down. Troll above fish, get your wish. Troll too deep, fall asleep.

Where Is That Fish?

- The form of each arch suggests where a fish is, and whether it is active or inactive
- A rounder, flatter arch suggests a fish more directly under the boat. So does a stronger echo
- A sharp-pointed arch suggests a fish off to the side of the boat. So does a weaker echo
- Inactive fish produce a clean, symmetrical arch.
- Active fish yield an irregular arch, trailing to one side

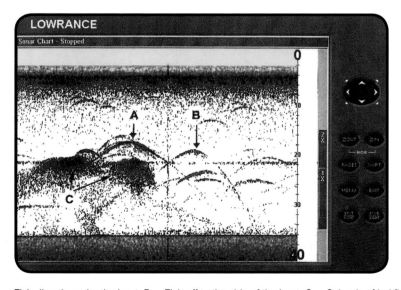

A = Fish directly under the boat B = Fish off to the side of the boat C = Schools of baitfish

How Big Is That Fish?

"Humongous fish on the screen! Let's catch him!" It's fun to guess the size of a fish by the size of its arch on the screen. It's also futile. Deducing a fish's bulk by its blip is like guessing a river's source by staring at its mouth. Can't be done.

The length of a fish's arch tells us how long that fish stayed in the sonar beam. Nothing more. The longer in the beam, the larger the arch. One fish might linger beneath your boat. That fish looks large on your screen. Another fish might spook. That fish looks small.

Plus, if you set your depthsounder's gain to "Manual" and cranked up the sensitivity, the depthsounder's software may magnify a faint echo into a strong arch. Makes sense, right? Well, it's even more complicated.

A small trout swimming for a while directly beneath your boat will echo longer and produce a bigger arch than a large trout swimming off to the side. Out there, on the edge of the sonar cone, a trout isn't in the beam long enough to produce much of an echo.

Remember the earlier admonition, "Turn Fish ID off"? The "Fish ID" feature reads signal strength to paint big and little fish icons on the screen. Here's the problem: A palm-sized crappie whose air bladder is expanding may yield a stronger echo than a slab crappie whose air bladder is contracting. An air bladder expands as a fish rises in the water column. It shrinks as the fish descends.

Depth plays a role, too. Since sound waves weaken as they pass through water, deep fish may echo faintly, even though they're large. Another problem: Since a sonar cone widens with depth, deep fish often stay in the cone longer than shallow fish. These deep fish appear as larger arches on your screen, even though they may be the same size as the shallow fish.

New depthsounders, with DSP (digital signal processing), automatically dial up the gain to cope with these problems. This software is good, but imperfect.

A low-frequency transducer, say 50 kHz, with its wide beam, will paint a wider fish arch than a high-frequency transducer, say 200 kHz, with its narrow beam. Why? The fish stays in the beam longer.

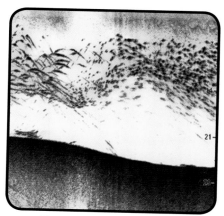

This Raymarine screen shows largemouth bass chasing bait.

Last, several small fish tightly schooled may appear on your screen as one big fish. So the answer to, "How big is that fish?" is often, "Who knows?"

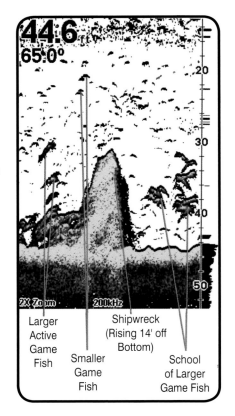

Larger Active Game Fish

Smaller Game Fish

Shipwreck (Rising 14' off Bottom)

School of Larger Game Fish

What Fish Is That?

Commercial fishermen can identify schools of some fish species by the fish's signature on the screen. They can also ID baitfish, shrimp, debris … with their $20,000 array of several depthsounders and U.S. Navy-quality transducers costing more thousands.

In shallow water, with our more reasonably priced depthsounders, we sports anglers can learn to ID some blips, too. All we need is a rod to catch the fish, or an underwater camera.

Consider acquiring a 7" or 10" full-color, flat-screen monitor with adjustable brightness and contrast; a camera with lights, on a 75' cable (22.5 m); a built-in 12 volt/9 amp battery; and a battery charger. Aqua-Vu and Vexilar make good cameras. You can display Vexilar Fish Scout camera images on your cell phone or tablet computer.

When you see what you suspect is a school of fish on your screen, lower a bait. If the fish won't bite, lower your camera. When you have identified what you're looking at, jot down some notes and save the screen shot to an MMC/SD card, via "Copy file."

Back at your computer, upload the day's photo-screens. Then label each screen and its contents. Print the screens. Within a few seasons, you will have a good book of fish schools' signatures. Identify signatures of individual fish? Unlikely.

Waypoints Mark Fish

A depthsounder without a GPS is like a miner without a map. You might discover the Mother Lode, but how can you return to it?

Waypoints are to anglers what buoys are to boaters. Waypoints put us where we want to be – on the fish. Drift a half mile while fighting a big tarpon? A fish icon and waypoint #18 guides us back to the school.

Found a seamount yesterday on your depthsounder, loaded with king salmon? Waypoint #19 – King Lair! Want to cruise home with the least gas? Hit the reverse-course key.

Binoculars to your eyes, you see that anglers on the boat 100 yards (30 m) west of you are hauling up sea bass. If you have a multifunction screen and a rate compass connected to your GPS, you can pirate their hotspot. The compass allows you to overlay radar data onto your GPS chartplotter, via an NMEA 2000 network.

Scroll your screen's crosshair cursor onto the west boat's radar blip. Quick-save that spot as waypoint #20. Be there at dawn tomorrow!

Does your depthsounder have an SD memory card? Some depthsounder/GPS manufacturers provide software to convert a history of depth soundings into a bottom-contour map. Example: Lowrance's "Genesis Insight."

Fishing or cruising, GPS is our bloodhound of the sea. Don't leave the dock without it.

Quick Tips	Zero In

‣ *Say, "Marking fish 50' away."*

‣ *Dual frequency: Display split-screen images. Compare fish's arch in the wide cone to its arch in the narrow cone. If a better arch in wide, fish swims to the side.*

‣ *Avoid guessing a fish's size by its arch.*

‣ *To locate a fish in the cone, turn gain down. If fish disappears, it's probably off to the side.*

‣ *Fish shows in wide-angle cone, disappears in narrow-angle cone? It swims off to the side.*

‣ *Jot down your depthsounder's cone angles so you can use a table to estimate cone width.*

‣ *The wider the cone angle, the more likely a fish will appear deeper than it really is.*

‣ *Scan for fish with a wide-cone angle. Then zoom in with a narrow-cone angle.*

Read the Bottom

"Mark Twain!"

Wé've come a long way since a riverboat captain shouted, "Mark," and the bowsman threw a brick on a knotted line overboard, then replied, "Six fathoms and shoaling!"

Follow the Thin, Gray Line

How many fathoms under the keel? Easy. Bottom type? That requires some thought. Think of listening to the radio in a room with hardwood floors. Sound bounces loud to our ears. Then carpet the floor. Now some of the sound's absorbed, right?

Like a rug, a soft bottom absorbs some sound waves. Depthsounder software detects the lessened waves and paints the bottom accordingly. *Example:* On Lowrance and Simrad monochrome screens, hard sand paints as a medium width, faded gray band beneath the bottom line. Mud, loose sand, or silt, a thin, darker band.

Garmin, SiTex, and Standard Horizon monochrome screens paint a white band and line. For nearly all brands, the wider the bottom band, the harder the bottom.

Notes: A steep slope also produces a wide band. And a low-frequency beam paints a wider bottom band than does a high-frequency beam. To prevent confusion, pick a frequency and stick with it a while.

Circular fish flasher: the harder the bottom, the thinner the bottom line, without a long tail behind it. A thick line indicates mud or silt.

Depthsounders find kingfish in the Gulf Stream.

Read Weeds

Weeds return fairly strong signals. If you have owned an aquarium, you've seen the billions of tiny air bubbles that cover underwater plants as they photosynthesize. In rivers, bays, and lakes, sound waves bounce off these bubbles.

Although the bubbles rise straight to the surface, they may appear on our screen as slanted lines or dots as the boat passes quickly over the weed bed. Weedbed signature: a series of ragged vertical or slanted lines along the bottom, interspersed with dots (from bubbles).

A bait ball swims above weeds on this Raymarine e125.

Trick: Adjust grayline strength last, after you adjust other features. This will yield the best bottom picture.

Hard Bottom or Soft Bottom?

Unlike a baseball coach on the first base line, we anglers cannot pat bottoms on the water. We can try two tricks, though, to deduce bottom hardness.

The greater the difference between your screen's numerical depth readout and its painted, bottom-line depth, the softer the bottom. Here's why: Numerical depth comes from a maximum density within the ocean floor. This could be 4' (1.2 m) deep in the mud.

This Lowrance X-107C screen paints fish over a hard reef

Your screen's painted-line depth comes from the surface of the sea floor, where mud and water meet. Why do software engineers program the depthsounder to paint this shallowest depth? Because most boaters fear running aground more than they fear going fishless.

So when digital depth reads deeper than painted depth, suspect a mushy bottom. When the two depths agree, suspect a hard bottom.

Photo by US Fish & Wildlife Service

The latest broadband depthsounders even ping bottom dwellers, like these walleye.

Outsmart Auto-Adjust Software

Some depthsounders, especially pricier models, defeat our desire to identify the bottom type. They do this because they're programmed to keep things easily viewable on our screen.

As bottom type changes, these units automatically change their gain (sensitivity). Screen stays clean. But the nature of the bottom remains hidden.

We can use this software to our advantage. With depthsounder in "Auto" mode, summon the sensitivity bar onto your screen. As your boat passes from hard bottom to soft bottom, watch the sensitivity bar lengthen to compensate for the change. If the sensitivity bar shortens, the bottom has grown harder.

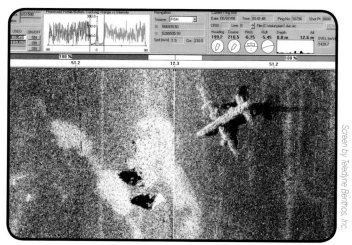

This side scan image shows an airplane
on the bottom of Lake Washington.

Study the Amplitude Bar

Another trick: Keep an eye on the amplitude bar at the right of your screen. Amplitude – a fancy word for strength. This bar shows the strength of the next returning signal. The amplitude bar widens as the bottom hardens, narrows as the bottom softens.

Color screens will paint hot hues on the amplitude bar for hardening bottoms, cool hues for softening bottoms. Red/orange: hard. Blue/green: soft. Note: The bar shows us relative bottom densities, not definite bottom types. Bar narrows or lightens: We may not know if the bottom is mud or silt, but we do know it's softer than it was a while ago.

| **Carry A Poke Pole** | If you fish shallow, murky water, here's an easy way to learn what various bottom types look like on your screen. Poke the bottom. Mud, sand, rock, shell – you'll identify |

each as easily as a chef feels a lump in the dough.

A 14' (4.2 m) painter's aluminum extension handle works fine. In saltwater, an 18' (5.4 m) stainless-steel golf ball retriever resists corrosion. You'll be surprised how accurately your hands can ID what the pole telegraphs up.

In clear water, Polaroid sunglasses let us compare the bottom to the screen. Seek out weeds, oyster beds, reefs... Poke them. Study their signatures. After a few fishing trips, you will recognize their tell-tale patterns on your screen.

Tech Talk | Gain

Depthsounder owner manuals tell us to, "Turn up the gain to see more fish." Gain is like the volume control on a hearing aid. Some manuals call it, "sensitivity," the ability to receive echoes. "Auto" mode sets the initial gain high. "Manual" mode on most depthsounders offers a slide scale, 1 to 10. You have two ways to optimize the gain yourself:

Switch to "Manual" mode. Set the gain at 100%. Then back off until you're satisfied with your screen's appearance.

Switch to "Manual" mode. Set range to three times the bottom depth. Turn the gain up until a second bottom appears on the screen. Reset range to actual bottom depth. Good detail will remain on the screen.

The second sound wave hit sea bottom, bounced back to the boat, hit the boat bottom, travelled back to the sea bottom, then bounced back to the transducer.

Because this second wave travelled twice as far as the first wave, the laws of physics state that it will be four times as weak as the first wave. It will appear lightly on your screen and won't offend your eye. The fish you will now see (due to the higher sensitivity) will please your eye.

Trick: Looking for fish near the sea surface? Turn gain down, to lessen surface clutter.

Lucie Fritz caught this 6 lb. largemouth shallow, in the Columbia River.
No depthsounder needed. . . this time.

Gain Data On Bottom Type

Beginning anglers set their depthsounder's gain (sensitivity) too low. They like a nice, clean screen. Pro anglers set the gain high – 70% to 90% of maximum. They tolerate some clutter. That's why they see more fish.

If the clutter runs deep, reduce gain until the clutter lessens, yet fish remain. If this doesn't work, and you have a dual-frequency depthsounder, switch to the lower frequency.

Note: No matter where you set the gain (sensitivity), your depthsounder sends out the same amount of power. Gain just controls how much the depthsounder amplifies each returning signal.

In your efforts to clean up your screen, never trade a clean screen for fish. Learn to recognize surface clutter or electrical interference on the screen.

Then learn to ignore it. "Hey, what are those bigger marks amid the clutter? Fish!"

When You Hit Rock Bottom...

As the Aussies say, "No worries, mate!" You won't hit rock bottom once you learn to recognize rocks on your screen. A rocky bottom often paints a second bottom line.

Suspect rock, but see no second line? Set your depthsounder's gain (sensitivity) control to "Manual." Turn up the gain. Study your screen for a second line.

On monochrome screens, a thick, light gray band beneath the bottom line indicates a hard bottom – gravel, rock, coral reef, oyster bed, shell bottom, or clay.

In auto-mmode, most new depthsounders paint different colors for different densities. The hotter the color, the harder the bottom.

Bottom Echo Colors on Lowrance, Simrad, and Northstar Screens

- A wide, yellow band denotes the strongest echo. Example: rocks.
- Orange, a less strong echo. Example: a shell bottom.
- Red, a medium echo. Example: submerged timber.
- Light red suggests a bottom of medium density. Example: clay or hard sand.
- Very light red or orange means a low-density bottom. Example: soft sand.
- Blue denotes the weakest signal. Example: mud, silt.

Lowrance LCX Depthfinder
(color shows echo strength)

Weakest Returns   Strongest Returns

Find a coral reef or gravel bar? To get a good picture of it in your mind, pass over it several times from different directions. Carry marker buoys aboard to define the structure before you waypoint it.

Caution: In wind and waves, it's easy to mistake a rippled bottom for rocks. A boat pitching and heaving in rough water will produce a wavy bottom on the screen. Only high-end depthsounders, like Furuno's WASSP unit, provide heaving compensation.

Fish flashers, like Vexilar's, paint a hard bottom red, a medium-density bottom orange, and a soft bottom green. Ice anglers like flashers. They can ID a soft bottom where dying weeds deplete oxygen. A good place not to drill.

Match Boat Speed to Bottom Slope

A steeply sloping bottom creates a more questionable line on your screen than a flat bottom. Is it really steep? A fast boat crossing a 45-degree slope paints a picture of a sharply sloping bottom. Why? The screen image compresses horizontally.

A slow boat crossing the same slope paints a gradually sloping bottom. The screen image stretches out.

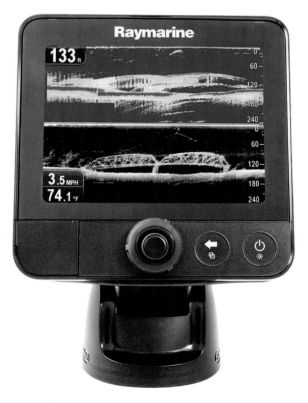

This Raymarine Dragonfly split screen shows a
sunken bridge, via a regular sonar beam (top)
and a CHIRP sonar beam (bottom).

The sonar pulse rate (ping speed) also affects slope accuracy. Given a constant boat speed, quick pulses paint a gradual slope; slow pulses, a steep slope. Why steep? With few pulses over the slope, the drop-off seems sudden.

The factory usually sets ping speed at 50%. You can vary ping speed from this default setting, via a pop-up menu. The faster you cruise, the higher the ping speed you need. But if you set ping speed too fast, you may get noise on your screen.

Commercial fishermen's high-end depthsounders monitor the boat's speed via GPS. We call this feature, "time variable gain." These sounders automatically correlate boat speed to chart speed and ping speed. A given fish's echo appears the same size, no matter how deep that fish swims. Few sportfishing units do this.

Trick: Over a known, hard bottom, when numerical depth and painted depth differ by more than several feet, suspect a sharp slope.

Only when boat speed and pulse rate are in perfect synchrony does the screen show the true angle of a slope. See a steep shoreline? Suspect its slope continues into the water? Increase ping speed.

Beware the Blind Zone

Bottom slope steep? Bottom plunges over an underwater cliff and into the abyss? Remember: To protect you from running aground, your screen will paint just the shallowest depth in the cone.

Fish near the deeper end of the cliff, below the painted bottom depth, will remain invisible, even though they are in the sonar beam.

Furuno calls this, "target masking." Anglers call it the "blind zone," or the "dead zone." Fish in this blind zone may show up later on your screen, as you pass down the drop-off and circle back. The wider the cone angle, the greater the possible blind zone.

Tricks: To see some fish in the blind zone, increase the sonar's pulse rate. *Also*: Zigzag slowly over the drop-off to examine it from various angles.

Consider Side-Scan Sonar

Want photo-like pictures of the seabed? How about seeing fish to the side? In front of you? Consider side-scan sonar. Treasure hunters have used side-scan for years. It works like an underwater radar, but with sound pulses instead of electromagnetic pulses.

A transducer containing several crystals shoots two narrow beams, one to each side, that cover 360 degrees, or any arc you choose. You can also choose

Digital depth & painted depth agree, indicating a
rock reef. Screen — Lowrance HDS 5.

distance and frequency – 455 kHz for more distance; 800 kHz for more detail, but less distance.

Since vertical targets reflect sonar signals stronger than flat targets, the depthsounder can use echo strength to paint images. Strong echo, light pixels. Weak echo, darker pixels. Software then adds shadows to the underwater scene.

Humminbird offers a Quadra-Beam depthsounder. This unit shoots two beams downward and a beam to each side. These side beams go out about 2 times the depth of the water, up to about 250' (75 m). Trees look like trees, complete with shadows.

Multibeam sonar goes even further: Humminbird offers 360-degree sonar imaging – look forward, backward, and to each side over a 300' (90 m) wide circle. The transducer extends into the water on a transom-mount pole and rotates. Before cruising, you pull the pole out of the water. To employ 360 imaging, you'll need a side-imaging fish-finder screen.

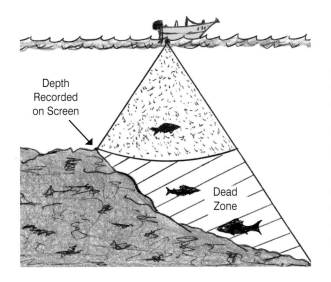

The Dead Zone

Over a sloping bottom your depthfinder may show the shallowest depth in the sonar cone as the overall depth on the screen.

Fish swimming deeper than this screen depth may remain invisible, even though they are inside the cone.

The steeper the slope or the wider the cone the larger the potential dead zone.

Furuno offers forward-looking sonar and searchlight sonar. To determine target depth, forward looking sonar measures the angle between the sea surface and the target. This works well when the bottom slopes up. Flat bottoms, not so good. Searchlight transducers scan 360 degrees.

Sideimagingsoft.com offers a forum for Humminbird users to discuss their side-scan results. This excellent website interprets hundreds of screen shots and alerts users to software updates.

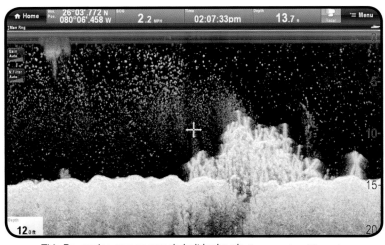

This Raymarine screen reveals bait by brush. *Screen courtesy of Raymarine*

Drew Fritz landed this 10 lb. silver at Sekiu, WA.

View the Bottom In 3D

Viewing a 3D school of fish is as much fun as watching a 3D movie. Side-scan/structure-scan sonar provides depth perception to our depthsounder. Lowrance and Simrad offer Structure Scan (side-scan and look ahead, to 250'; 75 m) to create 3D images of the bottom. Humminbird offers Down Scan. All of these scans work best at boat speeds less than 10 knots.

The 3D transducers emit sound waves in razor-thin slices. Depthsounder software then builds a 3D, photo-negative image of the bottom. On the screen, a sunken ship looks like a ship – a ghostly, skeleton ship.

Suspect walleye suspended near the bottom? Like a doctor looks for suspicious spots on an X-ray, we look for telltale shadows on the screen – fish shadows. The farther the shadow from the fish, the farther above the bottom the fish swims.

A split-screen proves handy for any of these advanced units – find the walleye shadow in the 3D window; zoom in on the walleye via the regular window.

This is SCUBA diving without getting wet! Note: Structure-scan usually paints fish as blobs instead of arches.

Quick Tips	Read the Bottom

- *A soft bottom absorbs sound waves. Weak echo. Cool colors.*
- *A hard bottom reflects sound waves. Strong echo. Hot colors.*
- *Monochrome screen: The lighter the gray, the denser the bottom.*
- *The wider the band beneath the bottom line, the harder the bottom.*
- *In manual mode, turn up the gain. If your screen shows a second bottom line, the bottom is hard.*
- *Depthsounder in auto mode: Study the screen's sensitivity (gain) bar. If the sensitivity bar shortens, the bottom has grown harder.*
- *Watch the screen's amplitude bar (far right side). The wider the bar, the harder the bottom directly under the boat.*
- *Compare digital depth with pictured depth. The greater the difference, the softer the bottom, or the steeper the bottom.*
- *Slow down cruising across slopes.*
- *To reveal fish in the blind zone, increase sonar's ping rate.*
- *Zigzag over a steep slope to reveal fish in the blind zone.*
- *In 3D mode, study the bottom for fish shadows.*

Mount the Transducer

Fishfinder: A gadget that proves some fish won't bite.

O ne might guess that the box behind the screen would prove to be the critical part of this gadget we call a depthsounder. That guess would be wrong.

Find the One Right Place The transducer proves to be the critical part. Behind every successful depthsounder is a properly mounted transducer. How important is your initial transducer placement? In one depthsounder manual, Lowrance Electronics devotes 31 of 92 pages to transducer mounting.

It takes 15 minutes just to read a Furuno Depthsounder Owner's Manual section on mounting a transducer on the transom. Humminbird claims 75% of owner complaints can be traced to a bad transducer mount. Let's make sure we mount it right.

Shoot From Beneath the Hull

Inboard engine? Transducer frequency about 200 kHz? Try a through-hull transducer with a threaded bolt shaft. Choose a spot close to the centerline. Tape the drill area to prevent chipping the gel coat.

Drill a hole through the hull, from the gel coat side. Unless your hull is flat, or you bought a transducer with an internally tilted crystal that matches your boat's dead-rise, add an outside fairing block to place the transducer vertical. Secure the shaft with 3M 5200 sealant, West System 406 epoxy/silica, or MAS Flexbond 5000. Tighten the self-locking nut. Do not over-tighten. If you trailer your boat, be sure bunks and rollers will not damage the transducer.

Shoot From Inside the Hull

Single-sheet fiberglass hull built without a balsa or foam core? You can shoot through the hull. This mount minimizes screen noise from water turbulence at high speeds. No log can knock the transducer off. A boat trailer cannot crush the transducer.

Many new bass boats shoot through the hull. The transducer sits well aft, to stay in contact with the water at high speed.

Single sheet aluminum hull? Radarsonics makes a 200 kHz alumaducer that shoots through aluminum with little signal loss. View Vexilar's video for proper installation (vexilar.com > Learning Center).

Does your boat's hull slant steeply? Install the transducer to direct the sonar signal straight below the boat. If your boat has a sharply stepped hull, Furuno recommends a mount in front of the rearmost step. That spot on the hull must remain in contact with sea water at all speeds.

Do not use RTV silicone. Epoxy is OK, but dries too brittle for boats that pound in hard seas. MAS Flexbond 5000 adhesive sealant is a better choice, especially for metal hulls. Epoxy is pretty permanent. Test the transducer to determine whether

For deep-V boats, some Airmar external hull transducers contain a pivoted crystal.

Drawing by Airmar.

Shoot Through The Hull

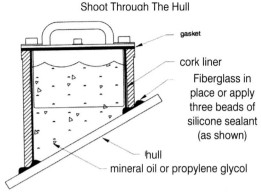

gasket

cork liner

Fiberglass in place or apply three beads of silicone sealant (as shown)

hull

mineral oil or propylene glycol

Airmar builds a shoot-through-the-hull transducer oil box.

Cross section of installed transducer—M260 shown

Diagram, by Furuno U.S.A.

shooting through the hull degrades your depthsounder's depth capability. Run the test in at least 60' of water (18 m), with the engine turned off.

First, hang the transducer over the side of the boat. Adjust clutter and noise controls to get the best picture. Then increase gain until a second bottom appears on the screen.

Second, bring the transducer aboard. Test it as it sits in putty or atop a water-filled plastic bag if you intend to install it in a sump. Furuno suggests filling the sump with antifreeze – propylene glycol. Do not touch the depthsounder controls. Does the screen still look crisp? Does the second bottom remain on the screen? Good. You can shoot through the hull.

There's Epoxy... and There's Epoxy

Airmar's in-hull transducer comes with a mounting tank. Glue the tank to the inside of the hull with 3M 5200 resin. Fill the tank with RV antifreeze (pink). Submerge the transducer in the bath.

Cored fiberglass hull: You could cut away the inner fiberglass layer and the balsa or foam core to form a pocket, then epoxy the sonar puck onto the outer fiberglass layer.

Epoxy steps: Clean and dry the area. Sand fiberglass and transducer face with 100-grit paper. Build a small dam around the area with putty or caulking compound. Pour the epoxy about 1/16" deep.

You must use special, manufacturer-approved epoxy that doesn't produce air bubbles as it cures. ACE (Acoustically Conductive Epoxy) is a good choice. To avoid bubbles, stir the epoxy slowly. Twist the transducer down to squeeze out any bubbles. Weight the transducer until the epoxy dries.

What if you epoxy the transducer inside your boat and later need to relocate it? *Answer:* Acetone dissolves epoxy. Build a clay dam around your transducer. Pour acetone into the reservoir. Next day, scrape the epoxy away. Wear glasses and gloves. Can't find acetone? Fingernail polish and many paintbrush cleaners contain acetone. *Caution:* Acetone may degrade urethane coatings.

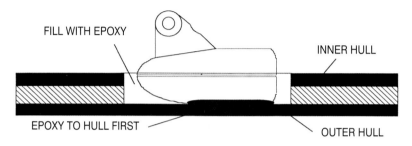

We can shoot through a fiberglass hull.

Diagram by Lowrance.

Consider Shoot-Through-the-Hull Disadvantages

You cannot later adjust the angle of the transducer for best fish arches. And shooting through a layer of fiberglass can cost you 10% to 15% of your depthsounder's power.

Multiple layers of fiberglass might cost you 20% to 40%. Why? Air pockets in the fiberglass laminations and sandwiched honeycomb scatter the sound waves.

Single-sheet steel hull? Double-sheet aluminum hull? Badly degraded signals. Mount the transducer outside the boat.

Wood hulls block sonar signals. Wood is too porous. Too many air pockets. Choose a bronze or stainless-steel, drill-through-the-hull transducer for wooden boats. *Note:* Wood swells when wet. It will crush a plastic transducer.

Shoot From the Transom

You want to mount a skimmer transducer on the transom? Good. Easy to maintain. Easy to replace.

You can use your depthsounder's "keel offset" feature to compensate for the depth of the transducer on the transom. Twin motors? Mount the transducer in between the outdrives.

Outboard motor: Mount the transducer close to the hull's centerline, but at least 6" (15 cm) from the prop's swing radius.

Mount the transducer.

Most props are right-handed. They spin to the right when observed from behind the boat. Furuno and Airmar recommend we mount the transducer on the starboard side, so prop wash will flow away from the transducer.

Vexilar recommends installing a transducer on the transom of a small, aluminum V-Hull on the side with the most weight. This is usually starboard, or driver's side.

Caution: Drill holes in the transom only after you've found a spot that paints good images on your depthsounder screen. Apply 3M 5200 sealant to the holes prior to screwing the transducer bracket on.

Reluctant to drill holes in your hull? SternSaver.com offers a glue-on transducer mounting plate, made of polyethylene/King starboard.

Test Your Transducer On A Sea Trial

Clamp a mounting board on the transom. This allows you to experiment to find the best spot for the transducer, side to side/up and down. Furuno suggests a simple sea trial:

On plane at modest speed turn slowly toward the side the transducer is on. Gradually tighten the turn. If the screen image improves, extend the transducer deeper in the water. If the screen worsens, raise the transducer. Avoid a roostertail.

If your screen still loses bottom, tilt the transducer's trailing tip down a bit, to increase the angle with the water.

This transducer is mounted under the hull at the aft step.

Or place a shim behind the bracket, thin end up if you run a small aluminum or fiberglass boat with a 20-degree transom angle; thick end down if you run a jet boat or a boat with a stepped hull with a 3-degree transom angle. No shim needed on a boat with a standard transom angle of 13 degrees.

To provide good signals on a fast boat, the transducer's trailing edge must be lower than its leading edge.

If these efforts don't work, relocate the transducer closer to the centerline of your boat. In short, experiment. Given enough sea trials, you will succeed.

Own An Inboard Or I/O Engine?

I/O engine: Mount transducer on the transom, near the centerline, but about 20" (0.5 m) away from the engine's lower unit, but not near the prop's cavitation bubbles, or the boat's strake or steps' bubble stream.

Stepped hull? Airmar suggests mounting the transducer in front of the first, aft step. Do not use a transom mount on a stepped hull.

Inboard engine? Avoid a transom mount. The propeller sits too far forward. Air bubbles will stream under a transom transducer. For inboards, try to shoot through the hull, well fore of the prop.

Depthsounders cannot shoot their sound waves efficiently through air. The face of the transducer must stay underwater on plane, free of air bubbles. On a boat with an I/O engine, mount the transducer inside the hull.

Wherever you place the transducer, make sure its cable enters the transom a foot or two above the waterline.

Keep Your Transducer Humming

- A transom-mounted transducer is convenient, but does require some attention.
- Spray transducer with water-based, anti-fouling paint, like Pettit's 1793 (pettitpaint.com). This paint uses zinc as the biocide. Never coat a transducer with ordinary anti-fouling paints. These paints contain ketones that will degrade the acoustic face of the transducer. They also contain metal-based compounds that will weaken the signal.
- If your screen turns to snow at high boat speeds, tip the back of the transducer down a bit. This cuts turbulence under its face.
- Above 20 knots, many sportfishing boats' depthsounders lose the bottom no matter how you position the transducer. A fairing block may help.
- If you cruise over 30 knots, consider building a pocket in the fiberglass hull to keep the transducer face flush with the hull.

Strap the Transducer On A Bow-Mount Motor

Do you want to strap your transducer onto the bottom of your bow-mount electric motor? Fine. A puck transducer is easiest. Bind it to the motor with wide electrical cable ties, or a factory kit.

Trick: If you mount the transducer slightly off to the side of the trolling motor, instead of on the bottom, the transducer's beam will rotate as you rotate the trolling motor. Turn the gain and range on high and you have ... poor man's side-scan sonar!

Downside: You won't know how deep the water is below your boat.

15-pound chum salmon in hand.
Photo by Alaska Deptartment of Fish & Wildlife

Shoot From a Kayak or Canoe

Kayak angler? Suspend the transducer through an existing drain hole. Most depthsounder manufacturers offer kayak scupper-mount kits. Or mount the transducer via a suction cup. Another way: Some small, portable depthsounders offer wireless transducers.

Canoe angler? Aluminum: Buy a side mount. Example: Sully's portable bracket. Or epoxy a Radarsonics alumaducer to the floor and shoot through the aluminum. "Zero signal loss." That's the claim.

Plastic or Kevlar canoe: Most transducers will shoot through Kevlar or plastic, but not carbon fiber. On the canoe floor, build a small circular dam with silicone. Let it dry. Fill the circle with water. Sit transducer in the puddle. Hold it down with a small sand bag.

Quick Tips	Mount the Transducer

▸ *Through-hull mount – Use a fairing block to shoot signals straight down.*
▸ *Inner-hull mount – Sea trial before epoxying.*
▸ *Use only special, transducer-friendly epoxy.*
▸ *Acetone dissolves epoxy.*
▸ *Transom mount – Sea-trial your new transducer on an adjustable board clamped to the transom before you drill holes in your boat.*
▸ *Transom mount – Place the transducer in between chines, close to your boat's centerline, but at least 12" (30 cm) away from a prop.*

Chapter 6

Transducer Troubles?

Surf fishing one morning, Clyde dove into the cold water to save a swimmer from drowning. That night, God spoke to Clyde.

God: *Clyde, you risked your life today to save a soul.*
        As your reward, I will grant you one wish.

Clyde: *Gee, I've always wished there was a bridge*
        across the Gulf of Alaska, so I could fish the
        other side.

God: *Clyde, that would be difficult. Isn't there*
        another wish I could grant you?

Clyde: *Well, I'd like to really understand salmon.*
        Why they bite sometimes, but not other times.
        Where they go each day. When….

God: *Stop! Two lanes, or four?*

G iven one wish, many anglers would like to know why their depth-sounder screen goes blonko at 24 knots. Fulfilling that wish would indeed prove difficult. But let's give it a try.

Bubbles Mean Troubles

Sound bounces off bubbles. Result: false signals. Keep your prop in good shape. A bent or chipped propeller blade produces billions of bubbles. These bubbles will clutter the screen, especially at low speeds when they linger under the boat.

Other source of bubbles: hull steps, strakes, rivets, through-hull fittings. Avoid mounting a transducer behind these spots.

Tech Talk | Save Your Boat From Electrolysis

"I wish I knew what's eating the aluminum away around my transducer." An easy wish, simple to grant.

A bronze transducer mounted on an aluminum hull equals a bad idea. Dissimilar metals in water become electrodes. Especially true in saltwater. Like a battery, the metals create electricity. This electrolysis will eat one of the metals away.

Electricity flows between the metals. This decomposes the more reactive metal – the transducer, the propeller, the hull. Saltwater speeds the process. Aluminum hull? Choose a plastic or stainless-steel transducer. Steel hull, plastic.

If you do use a metal transducer, enclose the transducer in a stainless-steel housing, isolated from the hull by a plastic sleeve. To verify that the transducer is isolated, check for current from the hull to the transducer housing, bare metal to bare metal, with a multimeter.

If you find low resistance, you failed to isolate the transducer. Electrolysis will occur. Rebuild the transducer housing. Note: Many Airmar transducers have isolation bushings that prevent metals from touching.

Electrolysis can eat up any metal.

A plastic Airmar transducer prevents electrolysis.

Transducer Problems, Q & A

Most depthsounder problems are really transducer installation problems.

Q: *When I turn my old depthsounder on, the range scale appears, but no echoes. Is my transducer dying?*

A: A transducer's ceramic crystal has a life expectancy of 50 years. But as a transducer ages, its frequency shifts a bit. With your boat in or out of the water, turn your depthsounder on and place your palm on the transducer's face. Do you feel pulses? Yes? Your crystal is OK. No pulses? Maybe a broken transducer cable, or bad plug.

Q: *I keep my 18' Lowe Angler moored on a lake. Twice now, muskrats have chewed through my transducer cable. This is getting expensive!*

A: The rats crave the salt in the rubber. Install a vertical bracket that lets you slide your transducer out of the water. Transducersaverplus.com sells them. About $75.

Q: *As my new Crestliner gains speed, my sonar screen gains clutter. Welded aluminum hull – no rivets. No strakes near the transducer. Stern mount. Stays underwater on plane. No roostertail. I still suspect the transducer installation.*

A: Your transducer suspicions are well-founded. Surely 90% of these speed-up problems are transducer-related. And aluminum boats suffer the worst. Air bubbles are plaguing your transducer. You have to move it. Fasten the transducer to a board. Clamp the board to your transom. Before each trial run, adjust the angle of attack, the depth, or the side-to-side position.

Q: *I use a 14' steel runabout in Biscayne Bay. My stern transducer doesn't give good signals. I'm thinking of drilling a hole in my hull for an external mount. What do you think?*

A: I think you should drill a hole in your head to air out your brain. Reposition the transducer on your stern. Or lower it on a bracket.

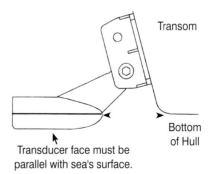

Transom

Bottom of Hull

Transducer face must be parallel with sea's surface.

Q: *I bought two identical fishfinders for my 16' walleye boat – one transducer on the transom; the other on the bow. You can guess my problem.*

A: Crosstalk. Each screen picks up the other transducer's signals, right? Trigonometry predicts that on a 16' boat, 20-degree sonar cones will begin to overlap at 45'. On-the-water testing shows they'll overlap at about 36'. That's because the cones balloon out a bit. Try raising the ping speed of one unit. If that doesn't solve the problem, call the fishfinder factory. Beg a trade. You'll have to change the frequency of one unit.

Electrical Noise

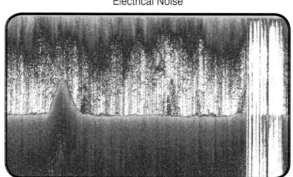

Repeating, vertical lines = electrical noise on screen.

Q: *Transom transducer. Cruising on plane, random dots fill my fishfinder's screen.*

A: Suspicion: When you accelerate, your transducer rises out of the water. Try extending it deeper, on a kick-up bracket.

Q: *Can I connect two depthfinder screens, same brand, to one transducer?*

A: Sure. If you have a NavNet-enabled depthfinder, easy. If not, buy a cable switch box.

Q: *I want to replace my Sitex fishfinder with a Garmin. Will the new Garmin fishfinder work with my old Sitex transducer?*

A: Maybe. Fishfinder manufacturers buy transducers from Airmar or Radarsonics. Check the technical specs of old and new units. Frequency and internal circuitry are key issues. Transducers with the same model number, but made for different fishfinder manufacturers, have different internal circuits. The power cable would be an easy splice to the new plug. Airmar has many transducer adapter cables. If you can't find an adapter and the transducer cable plugs are incompatible, say 5 pin vs. 6 pin, you'll need a splice kit. You'll have to cut the old cable to about the same length as the Garmin cable. By the way, these steps will void Garmin's one-year warranty. This sounds more and more like a bad idea, doesn't it?

This Airmar diplexer box switches signals from 2 transducers.

Q: *I have a Lowrance paddlewheel transducer to read speed. It seldom agrees with my helm speedometer, or my GPS speed window. What's wrong?*

A: Paddlewheels, at best, give us a rough approximation of boat speed. Ditto, a speedo. Believe your GPS speed.

Q: *I fish for kingfish in the Gulf. Since I began to moor my Grady White in the South Tampa marina, my sonar signal seems weaker. Why is that?*

A: Filthy face. Won't wet. Your transducer face gets grimy from gas spills, oil slicks, and the scum from algae die-offs common in bays. All degrade your transducer's sensitivity to returning signals. A Scotch-Brite scour pad, soap, and water cures this.

Q: *I epoxied my transducer onto the floor of my fiberglass boat. Works fine when I putt-putt along. Not so fine as I go on plane.*

A: As the bow rises, your hull is losing contact with the water. Try moving weight to the bow to level your boat out. If that doesn't work, relocate the transducer aft. Acetone dissolves epoxy.

Q: *I fish from a 36 Riviera. I just replaced my 500 W Garmin depthsounder with a 1,000 W Garmin unit. Not wanting to haul my boat out of the water, I hooked the new screen up to my old transducer. The screen worked awhile, then died. What happened?*

A: Your hot new model fried your old 'ducer's crystal. The transducer out of the box will work fine.

Q: *I just had my hull painted. I told the painters not to paint the face of the transducer. But they did anyway. Now my signal is weak.*

A: Wrong paint, right? Sand it off. The transducer's crystal is well protected in a hard, polycarbonate capsule. Just smooth the transducer face with 500-grit sandpaper. Spray with Pettit's 1793 water-based antifoulant paint.

Q: *I have an 18' riveted, aluminum Mirrocraft. Transducer on the stern. Poor signals. Should I epoxy the transducer inside the hull?*

A: No. Epoxy your right thumb and forefinger together, so you cannot carry out such an idea. Shooting through metal degrades signals. An alumaducer is too costly. Rivets or strakes are streaming air bubbles onto your transducer. Move it.

Tech Talk | Cut Your Cable?

Can we cut a transducer's sonar cable? Yes. Splice the cable with a Gem Electronics coaxial cable kit (gemelec.com, 860-683-0392). Shakespeare's PL-258-CP-G splice will also work (shakespeare.com). Protect the splice inside a Gem or Airmar splash-proof junction box, #33-035 (airmartechnology.com, 603-673-9570).

Caveats: Cut the cable at least 3' (0.9 m) away from the connector plug. The plug is waterproof. You must splice it back into the cable. The cable's impedance is factored into tuning the unit at the factory. Do not significantly change the cable length. Even the splice will add some resistance into the cable. If you cut the cable, you may void the factory warranty.

Shoot Through Ice

Winter angler? Shoot through the ice? Shovel the snow away. Pour a puddle of water onto the ice and sit the transducer in it. Seek clear, bubble-free ice. Avoid rough ice, smoky-colored ice, and ice with freeze cracks.

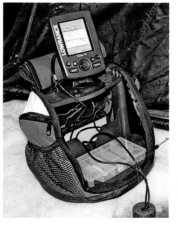

Afraid that at day's end you'll have to hatchet your transducer out of the puddle? Use antifreeze (pink, RV) instead of water.

Or build a wooden cross-bracket to hang the transducer through a second hole in the ice. Pour oil in the hole to prevent freezing.

Work tip-ups at several holes during the day? For mobility, fasten a depthsounder mounting bracket to a snowmobile or sled.

Ice fishing, look for clear, bubble-free ice.

Photo by Lowrance

Quick Tips	Transducer Troubles?

▸ *Mount the transducer to avoid bubbles from strakes, ribs, steps, rivets, and through-hull fittings.*

▸ *Metal hull – Choose a plastic or SS transducer.*

▸ *Before you drill mounting holes into your transom, clamp the transducer onto a movable board to experiment with locations.*

▸ *Two depthsounders on one boat? Run on different frequencies to prevent crosstalk.*

▸ *Transducers require special, water-based, non-metallic, anti-fouling paint.*

▸ *Splice sonar cable only with special kits.*

▸ *Wash the face of your transducer with soap and water.*

Troubleshoot
Your Depthsounder

Smelling liquor on his mate's breath,
the captain wrote in the ship's log: "Mate was drunk today."
Next week, it was the mate's turn to write in the log.
She wrote: "Captain was sober today."

S taring at your depthsounder, do you feel you've had a few martinis too
many? Dots, dashes, squiggles, blobs – appearing, disappearing. "Am I
looking at a thousand sardines? Or noise?"

As good as depthsounders have become, their signals can still cause us to
exclaim like the Amish, "It's a wonderment to me!"

Radio, GPS, radar, depthsounder – they're like hummingbirds at a feeder.
Each harries the others. Identifying the source of depthsounder noise, like
identifying birds, takes time.

Do You Have
A Noisy Boat?

Cruising along, do you see steady, horizontal lines
on your screen? Transducer problems. Screen looks
good at idle, but cluttered or lost signals when
you're on plane? Again, transducer issues. Air bubbles are degrading the
signal. Either remount the transducer, or add a fairing block.

Random dashes? Odd dots? These are either gadget problems or interference from another depthsounder operating at the same frequency as yours.

Test: First, turn off any automatic signal-processing software in your depthfinder. Second, manually set gain at 75%. Then turn gadgets on, one by one. Lots of gadgets, right?

Discount none. Electrical noise can radiate 10' (3 m) from its source. It can even paint phantom fish on your screen.

Second Sonar Noise

Run 2 depth-finders at once, at the same frequency? You may see noise on your screen. Solution: Add a switch. Run both depth-finders off the same transducer. Heavy, dark, vertical lines = noise. A nearby boat's sonar, with a frequency similar to yours, also produces this type of noise.

Trace Noise to Its Source

Electrical noise sprinkles dots and vertical lines on your screen. Like fog covers the bay, noise hides fish. When this happens, our depthsounder automatically increases its discrimination (noise rejection software) to filter noise. This eliminates weak signals from the screen – often fish signals.

We can test for this auto-shadowing. Turn the engine off. Do fish marks now appear? Turn engine on. Do the fish marks disappear? Aha! Engine noise.

Cut electrical interference with RF chokes.

Examine your depthsounder's power and signal cables for cuts or nicks. Noise can leak in. Signals can leak out. For some depthsounder problems, bent or broken pins in the unit's connector plugs may be the villain.

Consider an obvious source of interference: too much gain. Just as you hear static when you dial up the gain too high on a VHF radio, you'll see static when you dial up the gain too high on your depthsounder. Test by setting your depthsounder's "Sensitivity" bar to "Low."

Note: A depthsounder generates its own noise. It can interfere with your AM/FM radio, and GPS.

Sensitivity Noise

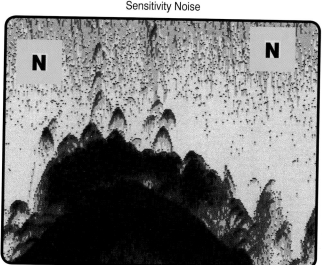

If you turn your depth-finder's sensitivity up too high, this is what you get.
N = Sensitivity Noise

Squelch Electrical Noise

Absent a nearby microwave tower, or a nearby boat's depthsounder with the same frequency as yours, the noise originates on your boat. Most boat noise comes from your engine's alternator and ignition. New engines have low RFI (Radio Frequency Interference) ignition wires. Old engines do not.

You wired your depthsounder directly to the battery, as the manufacturer recommended, right? Good. You wound excess transducer cable in a figure 8, not a magnetic-field inducing, round coil, right?

Power at the depthsounder reads over 10 volts? OK. First, carry out the tests in your depthsounder manual's troubleshooting section. If the manual doesn't help, maybe you can find the noise yourself.

Troubleshoot Electrical Noise

Noise Source	Solution
Boat's Other Depth-Sounder	Both units on? Cross-talk = noise (dots all over screen). Wire units to separate batteries. Keep wires apart. Choose transducers with different frequencies.
Small Motors	Blower, defoggers, windshield wipers – Reroute depthsounder wires away from devices' wires.
Tachometer	With engine in neutral, rev rpm. Noise (vertical lines when you rev the engine)? Aha! Twist the tachometer wires around each other. This prevents opposite currents from creating an electromagnetic field. Also, reroute the tach wires.
Helm Radio	VHF radios operate 156 mHz to 160 mHz. Route radio wires away from depthsounder wires. VHF coaxial cable radiates little noise while transmitting. Salt build-up on an antenna connector can cause static. Spray connectors with CRC electronic cleaner.
Radar	Keep radar screen and its wires away from your depthsounder.
Fuses	Take fuse holders apart. Clean. Tighten any loose connections. Replace fuses' twist-on connectors with butt-connectors. Seal the connectors. Jumping electrons are noisy.
Fluoro Lights	Switch to incandescent lights or LED's.
Microwave Oven	Other than your first mate, this is the noisiest spot on your boat. Keep the oven far from other electronics. Pop no popcorn while fishing.
TV	TV antenna amplifiers play havoc with depthsounders. Turn the TV off.
Battery	If your screen fades as the day progresses, the culprit may be a weak battery. If the battery voltage drops, test the alternator. Maybe it's not recharging the battery.

Noise Source	Solution
Battery Terminals	Corroded battery terminals cause connectors to float electrically, even though the battery's connections seem tight. When high engine rpm spikes the voltage, the electrons bypass the battery, jump into your depthsounder wires, and dance across your screen. Remedy – Clean the battery terminals. Coat with Vaseline.
Battery Charger	Onboard chargers are noisy. Reroute depthsounder wires far away from the charger and its wires.
Spark Plugs	Replace cracked spark plug wires. They leak noise. Buy ceramic resistor spark plugs (NGK R series, Delco R series, Champion SCA 9 series).
Coil	Add a condenser between battery and coil, on red (+) lead.
Alternator	Worn brushes or a bad diode generate noise (spikes on your screen at certain rpm). Add a noise filter between alternator and regulator, on red (+) lead. The NewMar Company makes a good filter. Or repair the alternator.
Distributor	Distributor cap cracked? Replace it. Then add a noise suppressor to the cap. Radio Shack sells suppressors.
Starter Motor	Add a condenser to starter motor.
Generator	Add a condenser between generator and ground.
Voltage Regulator	Does your screen black-out when you start your engine? Maybe your depthsounder is protecting itself from a voltage surge. Test your voltage regulator. Or run your depthsounder from a non-starter battery.
Engine Wires	Sparkle on your screen? Re-route depthsounder wires far from engine wiring harness. Add a ferrite bead to depthsounder's battery red (+) lead, near depthsounder. Radio Shack sells these beads, called RF (Radio Frequency) chokes. Choke the bead's plastic snaps over the depthsounder wire, like a clamshell. Or loop the wire through the bead several times.

Noise Source	Solution
Ignition Wires	Replace worn ignition wires with noise suppression wires. Wrap anti-noise tape around depthsounder wires. The tape is copper foil, backed with adhesive. NewMar makes it. Two-stroke, EFI outboard motors generate quite a bit of electrical noise. Run depthsounder power lead and transducer wire inside rubber garden hose.
Ground Wires	Your boat's electrical system must be well-grounded to water. No loose connections. Any depthsounder will malfunction on a "floating ground."
Water Pumps	Auto-bilge pumps can produce noise. So can deck wash-down pumps, livewell pumps, potable water pumps.... Reroute wires.

Transducer On the Trolling Motor?

Mount your transducer on your electric, bow-mounted trolling motor? Run that motor in variable speed mode (pulse modulation)? The pulses can generate noise that the depthsounder's power cable will pick up and carry to your screen. Result: vertical lines, clutter, or even a blank screen.

We call this conductive interference. It seems worst when the depthsounder's gain is high and the trolling motor runs slow. To verify the cause, run the trolling motor on high-speed bypass. If the screen clears, you've found the culprit – variable speed mode.

Another test: Disconnect the transducer from the depthsounder. Still see noise on your screen? Again, conductive interference from variable speed mode. A sometimes remedy: Wrap a sheet of rubber around the motor. Or add a ferrite core on your depthsounder's power cable.

If that doesn't work, test for a bad ground. Grab a multi-meter. Set it to, "Resistance," or, "Continuity." Connect one lead to the negative (black) post of your trolling motor battery. Connect the other lead to the negative post of your big motor battery.

A bow trolling motor can radiate noise to a transducer. *Photo by Minn Kota*

Any reading but zero indicates a bad ground. Ground the circuit with an 18-gauge wire and a 1 amp fuse.

Also check for current between the negative post of your big motor battery and an unpainted spot on your big motor. Your multi-meter should read zero here, too. If it doesn't, take your boat to a marine repair shop to repair the ground.

Powerful Motor, Powerful Problems

Own a power-hawg troller, like a Minn Kota RipTide electric trolling motor with 80 pounds of thrust? At high speed, electromagnetic energy can radiate out from the motor, into water and air. This overwhelms the transducer cable shield. The cable then absorbs the energy and scatters static over your screen.

If so, try this test: Unplug the transducer from the depthsounder while the electric trolling motor is running. If the static disappears from the screen, you've discovered the problem – electromagnetic interference, EMI.

If the static persists with the transducer unplugged, or with the trolling motor turned off, you have a different problem, probably in the depthsounder power line.

Remedies for EMI: Reroute the depthsounder power lead and transducer wire away from the trolling motor wires. Run the depthsounder off a battery different from the trolling motor battery. Isolate wires with a section of garden hose. Install an RF choke/ferrite core on the sonar power cord, near the depthsounder plug. And, most importantly, ground the trolling motor.

If these measures fail to banish the noise, consider switching to an internal transducer in a trolling motor. Minn Kota and Motor Guide offer these. Or run your trolling motor outside the objectionable speed range. Or remount the transducer on the transom and kiss the problem goodbye.

Combat Cavitation

Cavitation: the sudden formation and collapse of air bubbles in water due to turbulence. Common suspects: rivets, propeller, improper transducer angle. If the nose of the transducer angles too far down, it will create a pocket of air.

As the air bubbles pass over the face of your transducer, sound waves bounce off them. Result: noise. Cavitation noise often looks like a dark, cone-shaped wedge on your screen.

Remedies: Lessen the transducer's angle to the water. Most transducers work best with the trailing edge sitting slightly lower than the leading edge.

Another solution: Relocate the transducer to one side, or up/down.

Some conditions mimic cavitation: Rough seas, heavy boat traffic, and raging rivers pound air bubbles into the water.

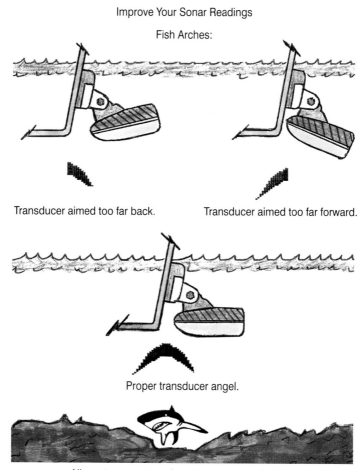

Improve Your Sonar Readings

Fish Arches:

Transducer aimed too far back.   Transducer aimed too far forward.

Proper transducer angel.

Align a transom transducer to prevent cavitation.

At Wits' End? Default

Tried everything, but your screen's still messy? Buy a small, 12V, motorcycle battery – the kind ice fishermen use for their electronics. Dedicate this battery to your depthsounder. Run the wires where no other wires go.

Or, if you have tried many adjustments from the depthsounder's menu and the screen still looks bad, you may want to scroll to the "Restore default (factory) settings" option. The resulting screen will show you whether you have over-compensated via too much gain, or via "Noise suppression" or "Surface clutter control."

Do you know someone who has a depthsounder like yours? Plug their power and transducer cables into your depthsounder. If it works fine on their boat, but not yours...

Big schools of pollock mark well on broadband screens.
Photo by Dave Wiley, Orion Charters, Valdez, AK.

Quick Tips	Troubleshoot Your Depthsounder

- *Keep depthsounder wires far from other wires.*
- *Twist gadget wire pairs around each other to prevent magnetic fields.*
- *Depthsounder and bow-mount electric trolling motor? Run off separate batteries.*
- *Keep radar screen and depth-sounder screen far apart.*
- *Wire your depthsounder directly to the battery.*
- *Run depthsounder wires through rubber garden hose.*
- *Keep the battery fully charged. If voltage drops, depthsounder power drops.*
- *Ground all boat electrical gadgets.*
- *Switch to resistor spark plugs & plug covers.*
- *Use noise suppression ignition wires.*
- *Keep battery terminals, fuses, and fuse holders clean.*
- *Check cables for nicks, crinks, and cuts.*
- *Check for cavitation at transducer.*
- *A higher frequency beam is less susceptible to noise.*

Depthfinder
Question & Answer

Q: Some days I stare at the screen and it looks blooey.
Other days it looks OK. What can I do about this?
A: Join Alcoholics Anonymous.

Hopefully our sonar expert, Groucho de Grump, can provide more helpful answers to common depthsounder questions.

Power Problems, Q & A

Q: *When I installed my depthsounder, I mixed up my power cables and ran them to the wrong battery terminals. Did I damage my depthsounder?*

A: No. Luckily depthsounders have reverse polarity protection. Next time remember: "Red Cross." Red wire to positive (+) terminal.

Q: *I found a short in my boat's electrical system. Could this damage my depthfinder?*

A: Yes. That's why you installed a 3A, in-line fuse on your depthfinder's red wire near the battery, right?

Q: *If I don't fish for a month or two, my bottom recorder seems to have less power. What's up?*

A: Nothing's up. Your battery's down. As voltage drops, your recorder's power drops.

Q: *To get to my boat's console, I need to run my depthfinder power cord and transducer cable through a rat's nest of wires inside my double hull. My idea is, it's the shortest route.*

A: That's a terrible idea! Noise will leak through. Forget cosmetics. Run your depthfinder cables outside, far from other wires.

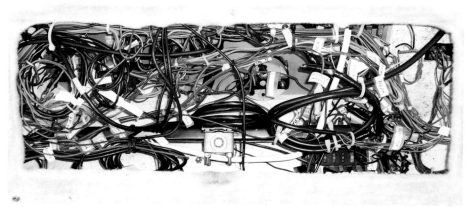

Route transducer cables away from an electrical rat's nest like this.

Q: *When I docked my 18' River Runner on Friday, I left my fishfinder on. Sunday, my boat battery seemed weak. Did my fishfinder draw it down?*

A: Monochrome fishfinders draw about 0.4 amp; color, a bit more; their backlight, another 0.4 amp. It would take a long time to draw a battery down. A more likely suspect: a dead diode in your old engine's alternator. A diode is like a one-way valve. It allows electricity to flow from alternator to battery, but not back. If the diode burns out, the battery drains.

Q: *I run my fish echoer off a small motorcycle battery. In summer, my screen flickers and dims. Recharging the battery solves the problem. I seem to need to recharge the battery more often in summer. Why is this?*

A: Batteries like temperatures that you like – comfortable, shirt-sleeve weather. They do not like to fry or freeze. In mild weather, an idle lead/acid battery loses about 6% of its charge per month. A gel/glass battery, about 3% per month. Double those numbers in the dog days of summer.

Q: *I'm tired of adjusting my depthsounder every time water conditions change. I want to fish, not fiddle with dials. Can you suggest a new, automatic model?*

A: I suggest a new sport. Sell your boat and take up golf. Whiners like you lack the patience for modern fishing.

Q: *I ice-fish with a Vexilar fish flasher. Battery's a small one. If I fished a long weekend, would my battery last three days?*

A: Sure. Even a little 9 amp battery will last about 30 hours of continuous use. A 7 amp, maybe 20 hours. Your battery will endure winter winds longer than you can.

Q: *I'm a weekend angler. Saltwater. I moor my Trophy 24' at a marina. Each Sunday evening, I remove my sounder to prevent theft. Last Friday, when I reinstalled the sounder, it wouldn't start. After I scraped some green gunk off the plug pins, it worked OK. These are gold pins!*

Spray CRC QD electronic cleaner on connector plugs.

A: Green tells the tale. As you remove and remount your depthfinder, friction wears microscopic grooves in the thin gold plating on the pins. In place of gold – green copper oxide. In salt air, enough voltage potential exists across the scored, copper pins to cause electrolysis, worsening the connection. Solution: Spray the pins with CDC electronic cleaner. Install a battery cutoff switch in the depthfinder's power cord. Add free-spin locks to your depthfinder's bracket bolts so you don't need to remove it. Or build a lockable cabinet for the unit.

Q: *I broke a pin on the power plug of my Garmin Echo. Can I repair it?*
A: Nope. Send it to Kansas City. Garmin will fix it.

Q: *I fish with an old, circular, flasher-style fishfinder. Sometimes, when I turn her on, she hums, but doesn't warm up. Then maybe she will, maybe she won't. Then, lights out. This frustrates me. Has this ever happened to you?*
A: Yes. But I don't date her anymore. Here's what's bedeviling you.

Your flasher's motor is current-sensitive. It needs amps. Your flasher's light is force-sensitive. It need volts. Test with a voltmeter at the flasher's plug-in. Low voltage? Check for corroded battery terminals. Or the flasher plug-ins may be oxidized.

This Humminbird 5976ci HD fish flasher is popular with ice anglers.

Q: *Before we leave the dock, I turn my bottomfinder on. Then I start my motor, a 350 hp, I/O, Merc V8. Then my bottomfinder freezes. Why is this?*

A: When you turn the ignition key, then release it, the collapsing magnetic field in the starter coil spikes the voltage, which then cascades into the power cord of your bottomfinder. Same thing sometimes happens to skippers who turn their engine off, then restart it. Either resequence your start-up, install a surge protector, or reconnect your bottomfinder to a non-starter battery.

Q: *Bouncing along in choppy water, my echosounder loses its screen. A few minutes later, when I turn it back on, it works. I'm at loose ends!*

A: Loose fuse. Loose plug. Loose battery connection. Corroded connections at any of these. For good measure, replace the fuse holder, too.

Drew Fritz's 15-pound. northern pike showed up on the 'scope.

Screen Concerns, Q & A

Q: *When I chat on my VHF radio, my fishfinder screen gets the measles. How come?*

A: Your fishfinder eavesdrops on your conversations. It hears the electricity your VHF antenna wire generates when transmitting. Separate the wires.

Q: *I boat on the Columbia River. When I drift-fish for bass along underwater walls and humps, junk clutters my screen. My partner says to get a new fishfinder. What do you think?*

A: Get a new partner. When strong river current hits underwater obstacles, turbulence churns bubbles and bottom debris into the water column. This shows up on your screen as clutter. Save your money. Dial down the sensitivity.

Q: *On a hot summer day, my sounder's face turns purple.*

A: I have the same problem. I hang a wet towel over my head. Do the same for your sounder–evaporative cooling.

Q: *My fishfinder has issues. Phantom blips appear, then disappear. What could be responsible for this?*

A: Issues, eh? Check your transducer cable for cracks, cuts, or a pinched spot. Check plug pins and sockets for corrosion.

Q: *I just installed a top-of-the-line sounder on my Bayliner 28. Automatic everything. Cruising at high speed, the screen shows few fish and an erratic bottom. Can I fix it? Or should I send it back?*

A: Keep it. "Automatic" seems the culprit. Auto-discrimination, auto-clutter control, auto-noise rejection... Either cavitation at the transducer or electrical noise is causing your depthsounder's auto features to kick in. Result: It's tuning out useful information, too. To test this theory, switch to manual mode. Have you considered cruising slower?

Q: *Last year my fishfinder screen was easy to read in the sun. This year, there's glare on the screen. I washed it with a bar of green soap. No improvement.*

A: In defiance of your owner's manual, you probably washed your screen with a gritty cleaner that destroyed the anti-glare coating. Mild soap and water works best. Lava soap is not. Call the factory. Ask about recoating. And stop complaining.

Q: *I fish Lake of the Woods. My echofinder screen seems to show less clutter in winter than in summer. Does sonar work better in cold water?*

A: No and yes. No: Sound travels slower in cold water. Although cold water is denser, and so sound should travel faster, cold water is more viscous. So sound slows down. Yes: Winter water has less algae and zooplankton to fuzz your screen. The thermocline breaks down, so mid-screen looks clearer. And far fewer boaters roil the surface water with air bubbles from their propellers.

Q: *I read somewhere that filters in depthfinders clean up the screen. My screen is too clean. No fish!*

A: A filter is software that detects questionable incoming signals and prevents them from showing up on the screen. Result: Interference vanishes, sensitivity remains the same. Examples of depthfinder filters: surface clarity control, noise rejection, discrimination, suppression. Unfortunately for anglers, these filters reduce the detail you see on your screen. A filter may interpret a school of small fish as just noise. To see more fish, dial the filters down.

Make Invisible Fish Visible

Surface clutter, or a thermocline, often masks fish swimming there.
To view these hidden fish, reverse your depthfinder's logic.

Method

1. Turn your depthfinder's auto-sensitivity off
2. Turn the manual sensitivity up, near maximum
3. Reverse echo color. (Normally weak echoes–fish–are black; strong echoes–rocks–are gray) Lowrance Electronic's Fish Reveal Mode does this reversal
4. Look for fish as faint echoes in a lighter gray background

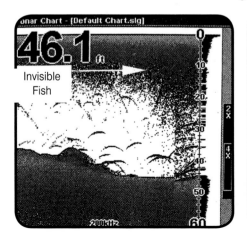
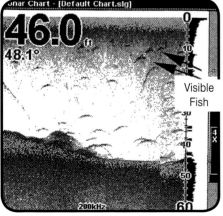

Q: *I moor my Seaswirl 24' in a Delaware Bay marina. I see surface junk on my screen before I even start my outboard motor. After I cruise a while the screen clears up. What changed?*

A: You changed surfaces. Bays, marinas, channels are busy places. Propellers churn billions of air bubbles into the water. Wind and waves pound the shore and jetties, further increasing bubbles and debris in the water. All this clutters your screen. Offshore, where you're cruising, the surface water usually runs cleaner. Result: clearer screen.

Other Problems, Q & A

Q: *My fishing partner says, "Depthsounders scare fish away." True?*

A: False. Fish cannot hear a depthsounder's sonar signals. For example: Freshwater bass hear well from 50 Hz to 200 Hz. A depthsounder puts out 50 kHz to 200 kHz, far beyond fishes' hearing. A study at the West Vancouver Laboratory, "Behavior of fish in their acoustic environment," showed no interaction between fish and depthsounders.

Q: *I fish an old mill pond with a portable fishfinder clamped on my canoe. Sometimes I don't even get a bottom reading. On a nearby lake I get a good reading. What's going on?*

A: The pond is probably so silted, the bottom has become too soft to return an echo.

Q: *My sounder goes dead when I fish in the rain. Next day, when it dries out, it works fine. I'm thinking of waterproofing the case with silicone. What do think?*

A: I think your idea stinks! That acrid odor you smell when silicone cures is acetic acid. The caustic fumes will corrode electrical circuits inside your sounder faster than you can say, "Why did I skip high school chemistry?" Fishfinders are vacuum-sealed with dry nitrogen at the factory. Once the neoprene seal deteriorates, back to the factory. If you try to reseal it yourself, with tape, for instance, you'll trap moisture inside.

Q: *I fish from a kayak. My echosounder is mounted on the gunnel. In choppy seas, saltwater splashes on it. I'm afraid this will damage the unit. Ideas?*

A: Saltwater damages all electrical gadgets. Remount your unit on a two-foot-high arm, like bass and walleye anglers use at their bow seats. Kayalu.com has a good one – Toughbar Ram Mount. About $20.

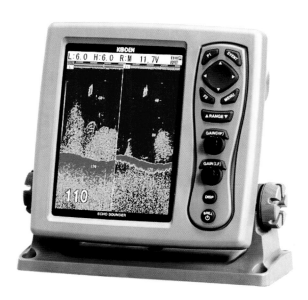

This dual-frequency Koden Echo Sounder marks fish well.

Q: *I troll for dolphin. My depthsounder shows boat speed. But it registers too low. What should I do?*

A: First, fine yourself $100 for not reading your depthsounder manual. Second, following your manual's instructions, key in a factor to calibrate boat speed to known speed. Best speed data: GPS.

Q: *I fish North Dakota's Red River. I own a high-priced depthfinder. Yet I seldom see a thermocline on my screen. Why not?*

A: Maybe the thermocline has not set up yet. Maybe you dialed your unit's sensitivity too low. Maybe a thermocline never occurs on this river. Maybe you need glasses.

Q: *Trolling, my dual-beam depthfinder works great. The wide beam sees lots of fish. But cruising, my screen loses the signal. I'm ready to toss it overboard.*

A: Before you do, hold your breath and count to a thousand. Explanation's simple: A wide beam has a hard time reading at speed. Frequency's too low. When you get up on plane, switch to your narrow, high-frequency beam. Even then, at some speed, increasing water turbulence at the transducer will kill the signal.

No boat troubles this morning. Let's fish.

Quick Tips	Depthsounder Q & A

- ▸ *Install an in-line fuse on depthsounder's power cable, near battery.*
- ▸ *Run depthsounder off a different battery than the big-motor battery.*
- ▸ *Cruising, choose a high-frequency sonar cone.*
- ▸ *Too much noise suppression will eliminate fish marks.*
- ▸ *Depthsounder loses power in rough seas? Check for loose battery connections, loose fuses, loose plugs.*
- ▸ *Read your owner's manual.*

Need A New Depthfinder?

*Depthfinder: An expensive device that tells
you how deep the water was where you ran aground.*

Buy Pixels and Power

Boaters used to say, "If you haven't been aground, you haven't cruised around." That was before someone invented pixels. The saying is simple: Buy the box with the most vertical pixels (picture elements). The more pixels, the better the bottom detail and fish arches. Horizontal pixels are history.

For deep fishing, buy power. Think of driving cross country, listening to your car radio. You receive the more powerful radio stations farther from their towers than the weaker stations. The powerful stations also resist local interference better.

For boaters, more power has five advantages: It drives the sound waves deeper. It penetrates dirty water better. Echoes return stronger, especially from great depths. Target definition along the edge of the cone improves, due to more power there.

And, because more power increases the signal to noise ratio, depthsounder filters can more easily separate strong bottom echoes from weak background noise. Result: less clutter on your screen.

Power Output	Maximum Depth in Freshwater	
600 W =	800' > 1,200'	(240 m > 360 m)
1,000 W =	1,800' > 2,500'	(540 m > 750 m)
2,000 W =	2,500' > 4,000'	(750 m > 1,200 m)

Notes: W = Watts, RMS (See Tech Talk, below). Some Furuno and Garmin depthsounders let us vary the power output: 1 kW, 2 kW, 3 kW. A narrow-beam transducer seems more powerful than a wide-beam transducer. Why? The narrow beam concentrates the power in a smaller area.

Tech Talk | How We Measure Power

Some manufacturers measure power (the strength of each sonar ping) in watts of peak-to-peak power. Other manufacturers measure power in watts RMS (Root Mean Squared), or more simply, "W".

Peak to peak or RMS – both measure the same output. But peak-to-peak power always reads larger than RMS power, often 8 times larger. Example: 30 W RMS equals 250 W peak to peak.

Like a keel works in tandem with a sail, power works in combination with frequency. A high-frequency sound wave requires more power to penetrate the water column than does a low-frequency sound wave. A 100 W depthsounder operating at a frequency of 50 kHz may rival the performance of a 1,000 W depthsounder operating at a frequency of 200 kHz.

For freshwater, 500 watts (RMS) works fine; for saltwater, 1,000 watts (RMS).

Buy Color Buy a color screen – pricey, but you'll never regret it. A color screen pleases the eye in all weather conditions. Compared to a black & white screen, a color screen reads far better in full sun.

New, transflective screens depend on sunlight reflecting off the screen to view an image. The brighter the sun, the brighter the image. A transflective color screen even looks good in dim light.

This Lowrance LMS-334c combines GPS and sonar.

Photo courtesy of Lowrance

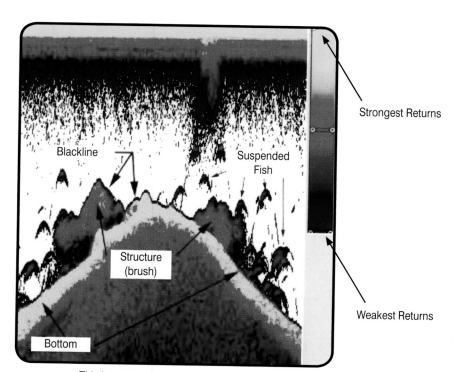

This Lowrance HDS 5 depthsounder uses color to denote target density.

Color lets us read the bottom better. Many brands, such as Furuno and Garmin, apply light tints to weak echoes. Sand and mud may show green, brown, or yellow. Strong echoes, from shells and rocks, may show orange or red. Check the screen's color bar.

Are you colorblind? You'll still appreciate the sharpness of a color screen. And colors will still exhibit different intensities to help you read bottom.

Color lets us interpret fish echoes better. Large gamefish often appear red or orange. Baitfish often appear yellow or blue. Some depthsounders allow us to choose a screen background from a palette of colors. We can pick a background that silhouettes fish best.

Caution: Pay up for quality. Cheap color screens (low pixel count, limited color palette) display poorly in full sun.

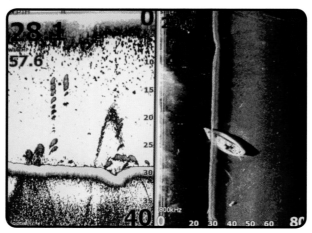

This split screen displays fish and a sunken boat,
on a Lowrance HDS 12 broadband sonar.

Choose Options

Just as cars come in several trim levels, depthsounders come with several options packages. What frequency transducer do you want? What cone angle do you want?

Alarms are useful. They alert us to changes in bottom depth (shoal alarm, anchor alarm), bottom hardness, temperature changes, fish that just appeared on the screen...

Do you want to display other data – radar, engine info, fuel flow, battery voltage, water temperature graph, weather, VHF radio channels – on a single screen? High-end depthsounders will. They will also allow you to scroll a range line down to the fish.

Do you need to share screen images across multiple units? Buy a NavNet type system. Images flow via Ethernet or Bluetooth cables. New units conform to National Marine Electronics Association network standards: NMEA 0183/NMEA 2000.

Maybe you want to send depth data to downriggers (example: via a CannonLink module to a Cannon Mag 20 'rigger). Minn Kota's i-Pilot Link connects a Minn Kota electric trolling motor to a Humminbird depthsounder/ GPS chartplotter. Motor Guide wireless trolling motors accept data from Lowrance HDS Gen 2 depthsounders.

Do you fish on choppy seas? Furuno offers, "heaving compensation." Do you fish for shallow-swimming species? Furuno lets us remove the zero line at water's surface. That line can be quite thick.

Many manufacturers allow us to paint a thin black or white line along the top of the sea bed to spot bottom-dwelling fish.

This Cali hali probably didn't show on the screen. But the sand bottom that halis like did show up.

Photo by Ventura Sportfishing.

Tech Talk | Pulse Width

Studying new depthsounders, you may encounter the phrase "pulse width," often called "pulse length." It's an easy concept. The depthsounder sends a burst (pulse) of electricity to the transducer every few microseconds. The transducer then pings the water.

How long does each ping last? "Hey!" That's short pulse width. "Hey-y-y-y-y-y-y-y!" That's long pulse width.

The farther a depthsounder must drive a sound wave, the more power required, which entails a longer pulse width. This forces the depthsounder to spend more time sending signals, and less time listening for signals. Consequence: lost data, less detail.

The very long pulse width of extreme-depth 'sounders (~ 70 milliseconds; 100 times longer than ordinary depthsounders) allows sonar to penetrate nearly 2 miles deep!

In single-frequency depthfinders, a high-frequency transducer usually has a shorter pulse width than a low-frequency transducer – another reason high-frequency depthsounders show better detail in shallow water.

The shorter the pulse width, the better a depthsounder can separate targets. At 200 kHz, with a short pulse width of 30 microseconds, a depthsounder can separate targets 2" apart. A fish 2" off the bottom will show on the screen.

At 50 kHz, with a longer pulse width of 1,600 microseconds, a depthsounder may only separate targets 60" apart (1.8 m). Fish blend in with the bottom. But this longer pulse width is less vulnerable to noise.

Expensive depthsounders can vary pulse widths. As depth changes, pulse width and rate change automatically. The deeper the water, the greater the pulse width provided. Some brands, like Vexilar, allow us to select pulse width.

Buy Broadband

Just as a car radio scans a broad band of frequencies to pick up stations, the latest transducers can sweep sonar pulses within a broad band of frequencies.

For example: A Furuno FCV 1150 deep-water depthsounder with a broadband transducer might transmit at 38 kHz. This model can slow the frequency down to 28 kHz, or up to 36 kHz. Each sonar pulse can go out at a different frequency. Shallow-water depthsounders (< 250' deep; 75 m) might sweep from 280 kHz to 380 kHz.

Since some species of fish show up better at one frequency than another, commercial fishermen like broadband transducers.

Lowrance, Simrad, and Furuno call their new units, "Broadband." Garmin calls theirs, "Spread Spectrum." Raymarine, "Dragonfly." All operate nearly hands-free. Their advanced signal processors separate targets within inches of one another. Touch-screen commands make it easy to refine the display.

Top-of-the-line depthsounders have software that can enhance screen images, much like Photoshop improves camera pictures. Lowrance's HDS series of depthsounders can superimpose bottom structure onto a GPS chart. Looking at the GPS screen, it appears you are cruising over the structure.

Note: GPS shows speed over ground. River anglers may want to know speed through water, to compensate for current.

Broadband's low power output reduces interference and noise. Software auto-adjusts gain and pulse width. Signal to noise ratios greatly improve. This allows a broadband depthsounder to receive much clearer signals from the water.

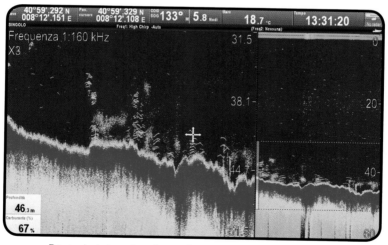

Raymarine's broadband sonar lets us spot fish near the bottom.

CHIRP! Crickets in new depthsounders? No. Just advances in U.S. Navy depthfinders. As the Navy declassifies technology, commercial fishermen adopt the new features.

Only after marine manufacturers reduce size and cost of these new units do we sportfishers benefit. CHIRP technology illustrates this.

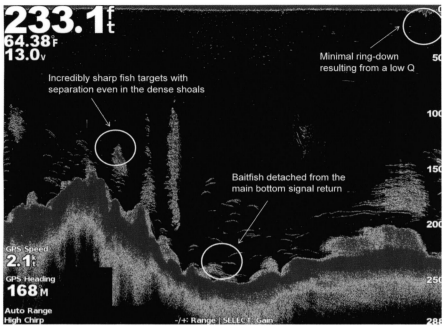

233.1 f t
64.38 °F
13.0 v

Minimal ring-down
resulting from a low Q

Incredibly sharp fish targets with
separation even in the dense shoals

Baitfish detached from the
main bottom signal return

GPS Speed
2.1 k t

GPS Heading
168 °M

Auto Range
High Chirp

-/+: Range | SELECT: Gain

5(
10(
15(
20(
25(
28(

Raymarine's CHIRP screen shows incredible detail.
Screen courtesy of Airmar.

CHIRP – Compressed, High-Intensity, Radar Pulses – marries with powerful digital signal processing software (DSP) to automatically cut surface clutter and water column noise. This allows us to turn the sensitivity up without blurring the screen with dots.

Think of CHIRP as second-generation broadband, sweeping a wider band with every pulse, faster, with more power, and better target separation. Side-scan sonar using CHIRP paints detailed bottom pictures. Note: Broadband/ CHIRP works best when you increase ping speed.

Although the Navy has used CHIRP transducers since the 1950's, they're still expensive. Some Airmar CHIRP transducers are 2' long, weigh 45 pounds, and cost $3,300.

Smaller sportfishing models are more affordable, but still spendy. Raymarine calls their CHIRP models, "Clear Pulse." Furuno calls theirs, "True Echo CHIRP." The True Echo version runs on high/low dual frequency, scanning 90 sub-frequencies. It uses Furuno's bottom discrimination software to estimate bottom type – sand, rock, gravel mud, silt – and Accu-Fish to estimate a fish's size.

If you fish a lot, you'll find them well worth the price. CHIRP shows bottom details far better than old units did. Fish swimming only a few inches off the bottom will show on your scope.

WASSP – Side-Scan on Steroids!

A New Zealand company, Electronic Navigation Limited (enl.co.nz), invented a Wide Angle Sonar Seabed Profiler (WASSP). This system uses 2 transducers (one sends, one receives) to determine the depth and hardness of the seabed ahead and paint a 3D image on the screen.

It uses a multibeam transmit transducer (112 beams) to floodlight the sea floor. Coupled to a rate change compass, this unit can compensate for boat roll and pitch.

Another single-beam transducer paints an ordinary bottom image screen. Another beam shoots to the sides. WASSP is the successor to sidescan and works like sidescan. True sidescan is different from side-imaging. It's more complicated and more expensive. Furuno employs a rotating beam WASSP in its high-end 3D depthsounders. Sportfishing models are soon to follow. Short of hiring Superman, this is as close as we can get to X-ray vision.

Select a Transducer to Match Your Needs

Sound: A bass drum vibrates only a few times per second. So it produces low-pitched (low-frequency) sound waves. These long, slow waves travel far.

A flute vibrates many times per second. It produces high-pitched (high-frequency) sound waves. These short, quick waves travel less far. Transducer crystals work the same way.

Water absorbs high-frequency sound waves faster than low-frequency waves. Rule of thumb: Use 200 kHz down to 200' deep (60 m), 50 kHz below that.

Low-frequency signals also define the nature of the bottom better – sand, rock, weeds in mud... But the lower the frequency, the more vulnerable your depthsounder is to noise, and the worse it performs at high boat speeds.

Transducers – Bigger, Better ... Sometimes

Like a jackrabbit's ears, the bigger the transducer, the better. The bigger a transducer's crystal, the more focused its beam. Doubling the crystal's diameter has the same effect as quadrupling the power output. And the more surface area a transducer face has, the better it picks up returning echoes.

Raymarine's A67 screen
paints a clean, crisp picture.

Photo by Raymarine

Raymarine's Dragonfly–one
joystick, easy to use.

Example: A depthsounder running 200 Watts through an 8"-diameter transducer (20 cm) will shoot as deep into the water as a depthsounder running 800 Watts through a 2" transducer (5 cm).

But sonar signals from a big transducer may not cut through the water as cleanly as signals from a small transducer. A big crystal requires a big transducer to house it. Possible result: water turbulence, air bubbles, broken signals.

Commercial fishing boats use transducers 3' (~ 1 m) in diameter, embedded in the hulls. Their searchlight sonar weighs several thousand pounds and costs many thousands of dollars.

Sportfishing transducers are a compromise – affordable; big enough to gather echoes; small enough to skim through the water without problems.

What if you choose the wrong transducer? Many manufacturers allow you to swap transducers, for a small fee. Or buy a multi-frequency transducer at the outset.

Considering a paddlewheel/transducer to show trolling speed? Your GPS is far more accurate.

| **Quick Tips** | Need A New Depthsounder? |

▸ *Buy plenty of power.*
▸ *Select the frequency you need: high for shallow water, low for water deeper than 400' (120 m).*
▸ *A dual-frequency split screen will prove useful for seeing fish.*
▸ *Buy the screen with the most vertical pixels. The higher the pixel count, the better the detail.*
▸ *Go with a color screen.*
▸ *Choose the alarms you'll need.*
▸ *If the screen will sit in full sun, test for anti-glare. View through Polaroid sunglasses.*
▸ *Trackback proves handy to study a recent screen.*
▸ *Broadband improves screen images.*
▸ *CHIRP yields better screen details.*

Lowrance's LMS-339c
combines GPS and sonar.

Photo courtesy of Lowrance Electronics

Chapter 10

Buyer's Checklist

"Sneaking a fastball past Hank Aaron is like trying to sneak a sunrise past a rooster."
—Joe Adcock

Shopping for a new depthsounder, you'll look for features useful to your kind of fishing. Let no fast-talking clerk slip a false sales pitch past you. Strolling the aisles or surfing the web, checklists will prove handy.

A depthsounder brings grand rewards — Jaclyn Humphrey, Joann Stoltz, La Verne Rettkowski with their coho at Sitka, AK.

Depthsounder Checklist

Let's review some features from earlier chapters. Later, with list in hand, you can visit a store to try out each depthsounder of interest in its simulator mode.

☐ Do you want a single-purpose depthsounder, or a dual depthsounder/GPS chartplotter?

☐ Do you want a self-contained display, or will you feed data from a black box to an onboard PC?

☐ Is the unit compatible with your GPS chart chips (Navionics, for example)?

☐ Where in the water do you want to look? Do you need a powerful (~ 1kW) depthsounder to shoot into deep water, or will a less powerful unit (~ 500 W) do?

☐ Will you flush-mount the unit in the console?

☐ Does the unit include a swivel/tilt pedestal mount?

☐ Do you need a quick-release mount to remove the unit from the boat?

☐ Do you need side-scan or look-ahead sonar?

☐ Do you want a unit with a SD/MMC memory card slot to record image history?

☐ Do you need a second, portable (handheld) depthsounder for a dinghy?

☐ How long is the warranty?

Note: You can display images from some transducers, like Vexilar's Sonarphone, on a smart phone or tablet computer. Many high-end depthsounders are just black boxes that feed data to a laptop computer at the helm.

Vexilar's portable depthsounder is handy for rental boats.

This Standard Horizon CPFi model displays both sonar & GPS, on a wide, low screen.

Screen Checklist

Where the screen will be determines what the screen will be.

☐ Do you need a low, wide-screen (Wide Video Graphics Array, WVGA, typically 800 X 400 pixels), or will a taller unit fit your console?

☐ A big screen must have a correspondingly big pixel count.

☐ Will your depthsounder sit in direct sun? If so, the screen will need an anti-glare coating.

☐ Can you view the screen well through polarized sunglasses?

☐ Is the screen backlit so you can read it in dim light?

☐ Does the screen have wide viewing angles (~ 80 degrees left/right; ~ 60 degrees top/bottom)?

☐ Can the unit reverse the screen scroll to view recent screen history?

☐ Do you prefer menu-driven software, or lots of buttons and knobs?

☐ Since we adjust sensitivity more often than other features, some brands offer a gain knob.

☐ Do you want a depthsounder with a touch-screen, a keypad, or both?

Note on touchscreens: Yachties have clean fingers. Touching their screen does no harm. Anglers have dirty fingers – fish blood, reel oil, salt, smelly jelly... So we need to clean a touchscreen a lot. The risk – unless we're careful, we could damage the screen's anti-glare coating.

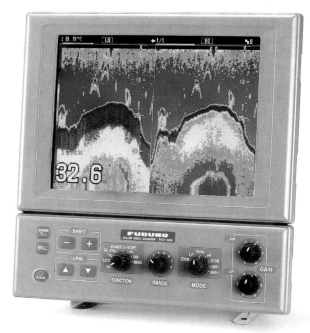

This Furuno FCV 1200 has dual frequency on a split screen, with push-button & dial controls.

Raymarine's e165 touchscreen display is easy to use.

Transducer Checklist

Depthsounder manufacturers offer many transducer options. Cone angles vary from 9 degrees to 60 degrees. Frequencies vary from 25 kHz to 400 kHz. Furuno FFS (Furuno Free Synchronizer) depthsounders and some Garmin units let us select any 2 frequencies, usually between 25 kHz and 210 kHz, while we're fishing.

☐ Do you need a transducer that shoots signals deeper than a few hundred feet? Choose 50 kHz.

☐ Do you fish both shallow and deep? You'll need a dual-frequency transducer (200 kHz/50 or 77 kHz).

☐ Does the unit's price include a transducer?

☐ Do you need an adapter to connect the depthsounder to a transducer built-in to a bow-mount electric trolling motor?

☐ Will you need to switch two or more transducers to a single depthsounder?

☐ Where will you mount your transducer?

☐ On the transom, inside the hull, on the outer bottom of the hull, on the bow motor?

☐ Do you want a transducer with a paddlewheel speed sensor? Surface-water temperature sensor?

Minn Kota/Motor Guide models with a 200 kHz transducer built into the bottom of the electric trolling motor housing are compatible with most depthsounder brands. Minn Kota's iPilot Link connects with Humminbird units.

The depthsounder/GPS unit (with Lake Master digital charts) relays depth and position to the trolling motor. The trolling motor can then follow a selected bottom contour.

Cannon's Digi-Troll transducer provides bottom-tracking data to Cannon downriggers. We can then program each downrigger to run its cannonball a set distance off the bottom.

Minn Kota sells bow-motor-to-transducer cable and connectors for most depthsounders.

Big schools of bluefish mark well on any screen. Photo by U.S. Fish & Wildlife Service.

Why Are Some Depthsounders So Spendy?

A high-end depthsounder can cost more than some boats. If $3,000 to $12,000 is in your price range, this discussion may interest you. Let's review what we get for our money.

Automatic: Just as a car with an automatic transmission costs more than a car with a stick-shift, depthsounders that auto-adjust gain and range, auto-filter out noise, auto-suppress interference, auto-cut clutter, speed signals in shallow water, slow signals in deep water, etc. cost more than depthsounders that make us burrow through menus to do these tasks – if the tasks are even available in a cheaper model. We're paying for computer engineers to write the complex software.

Touchscreen commands cost more than menu-driven commands. A multifunction screen networked to GPS, radar, engine sensors, fuel flowmeter, cockpit cameras... costs more than a sounder-only screen. A wireless network also costs more. Again, the advanced software drives up the price.

Screens: There are screens ... and there are high-end screens. Monochrome, 8-color, 16-color, 64-color ... 5", 12", 16" ... low-pixel density, high-pixel density ... wide-angle viewing ... anti-glare coatings usually reserved for Zeiss binoculars ... rapid-fire screen updates ... you get the picture. We get what we pay for.

Here's what tomorrow's depthfinder screen might look like —
A school of herring on a Furuno WASSP screen.

Need the power to penetrate 2,000' deep to find swordfish? Pay for the watts. Need to vary the power for different fishing? Select from an array of frequencies and cones in one giant many-crystalled transducer? Pay the piper.

Searchlight sonar is handy – 360 degrees. So is sidescan sonar and look-ahead sonar. While we're at it, let's view the bottom in 3D.

Then there's broadband, CHIRP, and WASSP. Clearly better technology. Ah, but the price. Depthsounders are really just floating computers. And, like computers, the more speed and cutting-edge features we demand, the more we must pay.

Are you an every-other-weekend angler? Probably pass on the high-end models. Everyday fishing fanatic? Where's your wallet?

Note: Before you buy read the reviews. Find hundreds of depthsounder reviews at amazon.com, Iboats.com, TheHullTruth.com, Cabelas.com, and BassPro.com.

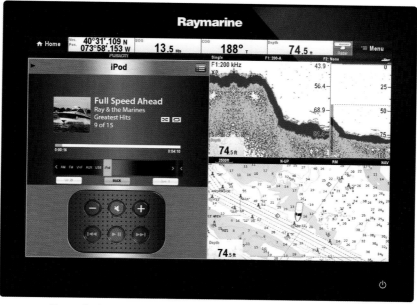

Raymarine's 165 model displays multi-screens — Chart, Sonar, Radio.

Quick Tips	Buyer's Checklist

> *Screen choice depends on screen location.*
> *The biggest depthsounder factor: Where in the water do you want to look?*
> *Try out a depthsounder in simulation mode.*
> *The right transducer is critical. Select one only after considerable thought.*
> *Weigh advanced features against their cost and your use.*
> *Look into your fishing future to choose a model to meet your needs.*

Appendix 1

Depth Formula: Acoustic Depth Measurement

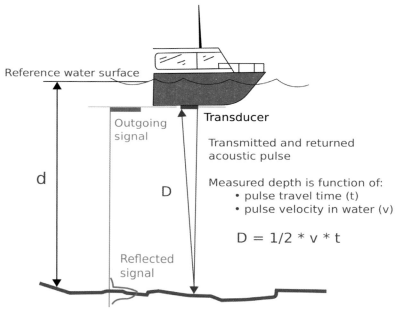

Reference water surface

Outgoing signal

d

D

Reflected signal

Transducer

Transmitted and returned acoustic pulse

Measured depth is function of:
• pulse travel time (t)
• pulse velocity in water (v)

$$D = 1/2 * v * t$$

Courtesy of WIKI Commons

Sonar Cone Side Lobes

Transducers

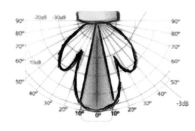

Wide Beam

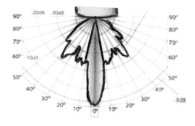

Narrow Beam

Diagram by WIKI Commons

Fish on the scope.

Screen shot by Lowrance

Tomorrow's depthfinder screen.

Furuno's WASSP model shows schools of herring in the Gulf of Alaska.

Appendix 2

Sonar Beam Coverage – Volume

As beam depth doubles, cone volume increases 8-fold.

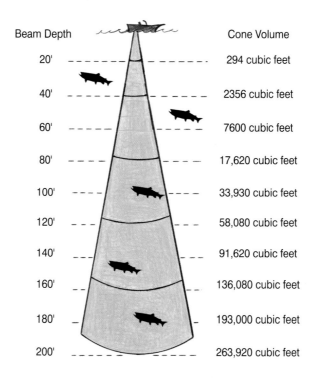

Beam Depth		Cone Volume
20'		294 cubic feet
40'		2356 cubic feet
60'		7600 cubic feet
80'		17,620 cubic feet
100'		33,930 cubic feet
120'		58,080 cubic feet
140'		91,620 cubic feet
160'		136,080 cubic feet
180'		193,000 cubic feet
200'		263,920 cubic feet

Transducer Cone Coverage Formula

You can find the diameter of a cone at any depth:
C = (0.0175) X (D) X (A) where C is the cone coverage (diameter of the cone's circle) in feet, D is the water depth in feet, A is the cone angle in degrees, 0.0175 is a constant factor (1 degree of cone angle yields a cone diameter of 1.75' @ 100' deep.)

Example: A transducer with a cone angle of 10 degrees, shooting 100' deep into the water would cover 17.5' of water horizontally.

C = (0.0175) X (100') X (10 degrees) = 17.5'
(Constant)   (D)   (A)

Sonar Beam Coverage

Diagram by Humminbird

Sonar Beam Coverage Table

Cone Angle	Strongest Beam Coverage
20 degrees	0.35 X depth, or 1/3 of depth
24 degrees	0.42 X depth, or 2/5 of depth
40 degrees	0.53 X depth, or 1/2 of depth
50 degrees	0.35 X depth, or 3/4 of depth
60 degrees	0.35 X depth, or 9/10 of depth
70 degrees	0.35 X depth, or 1/3 of depth
73 degrees	1.50 X depth
80 degrees	1.70 X depth
90 degrees	2.00 X depth
100 degrees	2.40 X depth
110 degrees	2.90 X depth

Example:
You are fishing in water 10' deep. The cone angle of your transducer is 20 degrees. The beam covers 0.35 X 10' = 3.5' across the bottom (3 m deep, 1 m bottom diameter)

Appendix 3
Free Lessons and Video Tutorials Online

Read Before You Buy

- Before you buy any depthsounder, read the owner's manual online to study its features and ease of operation.
- West Marine's online advisories, "Selecting a Fishfinder," and "Selecting a Transducer," at westmarine.com, provide good overviews.
- Boating and fishing magazines archive their articles. Power & Motor-Yacht magazine has archived many good articles on the most recent technology in depthsounders.

Transducer Tips

- At raymarine.com, click on, "products > fishfinders > selecting a transducer, or > CHIRP technology.
- Furuno.com offers good transducer tips. Click on, "learning center > Complete angler's guide to marine transducers."
- Check out garmin.com's "Transducer Selection Guide."
- Airmar (Airmar.com >FAQ, 603-673-9570, Milford NH) builds transducers, offers installation advice, and answers questions. Airmar sells only to manufacturers.
- Radarsonics (Radarsonics.com, 714-630-7288, Anaheim, CA) manufactures transducers, and offers online info. Sells only to manufacturers.
- Vexilar (vexilar.com > Learning Center > Read Articles/View videos) offers good instruction for mounting transducers.

Free Online Tutorials

Many depthsounder manufacturers provide free online lessons.

- Garmin.com's blog covers many topics, often with videos.
- At lowrance.com, click on, "support > knowledge base > sonar tutorial." Good info there to distinguish bottom types, bait, and fish. Or view Lowrance's free video library online. Lowrance sells 2 DVD's: "Understanding Sonar Training," and, "HDS Training."
- At saltpatrol.com, click on, "Lowrance Video Library," and, "Lowrance Tech Bites," to view videos for free. View a video that explains how to fine-tune Lowrance HDS depthsounders.
- At Bruce Samsom's website, doctorsonar.com, click on "Lowrance Electronic Tutorials," to view free lessons.

- Hightechfishing.com provides another portal to Lowrance tutorials.
- Humminbird.com explains searchlight sonar. Click on, "support."
- YouTube.com has dozens of depthsounder/transducer videos, ranging from installation to use. Some are good. Some are not.
- Lance Valentine's Walleye101.com site offers free video depthsounder lessons.

Try Forums

Threads in forums at TheHullTruth.com > Marine Electronics, discuss depthsounders and transducers a lot. Forum visitors either pose a query, expound on a topic, or critique a depthsounder. You'll find many threads on the latest, state-of-the-art depthsounders. The threads on CHIRP models are particularly good.

Furunousa.com/Support/Forum always has good discussions going on, especially about the latest technology.

Update Your Software

Depthsounder manufacturers offer free online software updates. Download the latest version to a SD/MMC card. Upload the version to your depthsounder. Updates are especially important for new models, which may have been released with a few flaws.

The maxim "When all else fails, read the directions" holds true for depthsounders. Lose your owner's manual? Manufacturers also offer free downloads of their manuals online.

Appendix 4
Depthsounder & Transducer Manufacturers

Airmar, airmartechnology.com, 603-673-9570, (builds transducers, sells only to depthsounder manufacturers), Milford, NH; at website, click on, "FAQ > Does Airmar have a transducer guide? > Yes"

Echopilot, echopilot.com, +44 (0) 1425-476211, Hampshire, England

Faria, faria-instruments.com, 860-848-9271, Montville, CT

Furuno Electric Company, furunoUSA.com, 360-834-9300 (customer support)/410-479-4420 Camas, WA; click on, "Recreational boats;" at navnet.com click on, "3D/tutorials/training videos," for Furuno lessons

Garmin, garmin.com, owns Interphase Technologies, 800-800-1020 (USA), 866-429-9296 (CN)/913-440-8280/913-397-8200, (all phone numbers for customer support), Olathe, KS

Humminbird, humminbird.com, 800-633-1468 (customer service)/334-687-6613 (sales), Techsonic Industries, a Johnson Outdoors Marine Electronics company, Eufala, AL; at website, click on, "Support > troubleshooting"

Interphase Technologies, interphase-tech.com, a Garmin subsidiary, 855-607-2541(customer support), Soquel, CA

JRC Marine Electronics, jrcamerica.com, 888-225-4472/206-654-5644 (both numbers for customer support), Seattle, WA

Koden Electronics Company, Koden-Electronics.co.jp, +81-3-3756-6918, distributed in U.S.A. by Sitex, Tokyo, Japan

Lowrance, lowrance.com, a NAVICO subsidiary, 800-324-1354/800-628-4487/918-437-6881 (customer service), Tulsa, OK; at website, click on, "Support > tips & tutorials >sonar tutorial"

Navico, navico.com, owns Lowrance, Northstar, and Simrad, 800-628-4487/918-437-6881/800-324-1356 (numbers are customer support for all subsidiaries)

Northstar, northstarnav.com, a Navico subsidiary, 800-628-4487/603-324-2043, Acton, MA

Radarsonics, radarsonics.com, (builds transducers, sells only to depthsounder manufacturers), 714-630-7288, Anaheim, CA, 92806

Raymarine, raymarine.com, (a FLIR Company), 800-539-5539/603-324-7900/603-881-5200 (all numbers for customer support), Nashua, NH; at website, click on, "Products > tech tips & transducers," or, "Service & support > FAQ"

Simrad, simrad-yachting.com, a Navico subsidiary, 425-778-8821 (Navico); at website, click on, "How-to videos," Lynnwood, WA

SiTex Marine Electronics, si-tex.com, 631-996-2690 (customer service), Riverhead, NY

Standard Horizon, standardhorizon.com, 714-827-7600/800-767-2450 (customer support), Cypress, CA

Appendix 5
Depthsounder Glossary

360 Imaging: Humminbird's scanning depthsounder; a 150' beam sweeps the water; we can adjust the sweep arc from 10 degrees to 360 degrees; transducer deploys on a transom rod

AccuFish: Furuno's icons that estimate the length of a fish

Acoustic: relating to sound

Acoustical interference: when turbulent water flows across a transducer's face screen noise results

Air bladder: a gas sac in some fish that inflates as fish swims upward, deflates, downward; sound waves echo off the sac

Amplitude: the strength of a sound wave, measured in decibels

Amplitude mode: a column at the far right of a Lowrance screen; previews strength of the next signal that will paint on the screen

Array: a series of crystal elements in a transducer that sends and receives sonar signals

A-scope: Furuno's horizontal amplitude bar at right of screen; real-time data; previews next echo; longer bar = harder bottom

ASP: Automatic Signal Processing; Lowrance's auto adjustment of gain, noise suppression, surface clutter...

Aspect ratio: the relationship between a screen's width and height; for example a 7" screen (diagonal) often has an aspect ration of 16:9, much wider than high

Backscatter: echoes scatter back to transducer; shows intensity of bottom

Beamwidth: the area inside the most effective angle of the transducer's sound wave; as frequency increases, beamwidth decreases

Black box: depthsounder box separate from screen; feeds signals to and from transducer and screen

Blind zone: dead zone; target masking; the area beside a ledge or steep slope where the depthsounder does not paint fish or other targets on the screen

Bottom discrimination: Furuno and SiTex software that shows the bottom type via different colors and their intensities

Bottom lock: feature that automatically adjusts the depth scale to keep the sea bottom on the screen; also called bottom track; flattens the sea bed

Bottom zoom: feature that zooms in on the water column near bottom

Brilliance: Furuno's term for brightness

Broadband: increased bandwidth for a frequency; produces a crisper screen image

Cavitation: the sudden formation and collapse of air bubbles in water due to turbulence; propellers, rivets, steps, and strakes can create these air bubbles that may show on the screen as noise

CHIRP: Compressed High Intensity Radar Pulses sweep over a wide band of frequencies to enhance screen images

Clear Pulse: Raymarine's CHIRP technology

Clutter: junk pixels on screen; from noise, water debris, another depth-sounder...

Colorline: shows different target densities by painting different colors on the screen, especially at the bottom

Cone angle: the signal angle of sonar that radiates from the transducer; wide or narrow cone, depending on the transducer's frequency; measured in degrees

Control head: the cabinet that contains the depthsounder display screen and software circuits

Crosstalk: noise on screen when one depthsounder interferes with another depthsounder

CSTN: Color Super-Twisted Nematic; a way to display data, producing better viewing angles

Dead zone: blind zone; area near a steep bottom or ledge where fish do not mark on the screen

dB: decibel, measures the relationship between power levels; practically, the strength (loudness) of a sound wave; also measures the gain (sensitivity) of a sound amplifier

Digital depth: depthsounder overlays a number on the screen to show depth

Discrimination: a depthsounder feature that suppresses noise

DownScan: down imaging; transducer sends sonar beam directly under the boat

DownVision: Raymarine's CHIRP depthsounder feature; synchronizes with a regular image of the bottom in split-screen mode

Down Vu: Garmin's term for painting picture-like images of the bottom

DSI: Down Scan Imaging; Lowrance and Simrad's 3D sonar

DSP: Digital Signal Processing; filters out noise and non-fish echoes; automatically adjusts gain and filter levels

Dual beam: a choice of two sonar beams, of different cone angles

Dual frequency: a choice of two sonar frequencies from one transducer; usually one high frequency, one low frequency

Echosounder: synonym for depthsounder

Electrolysis: ions flow from one metal to another through a solvent, usually water; this decomposes the more reactive metal

EMI: Electromagnetic Interference; electricity escapes from electric trolling motor housing and enters transducer cable

Fairing: reshape hull to change transducer's mounting angle; add a tapered block to change transducer's mounting angle

False echo: a very hard bottom echoes twice to produce a phantom bottom, about mid-screen; the deep scattering layer also paints a false bottom echo, mid-screen

FasTrack: Lowrance's amplitude bar

Fathometer: synonym for depthsounder

FDF: Furuno Digital Filter; removes noise and clutter to see fish better

FFS: Furuno Free Synchronizer; lets us choose 2 frequencies, between 28 kHz to 200 kHz

FLS: Interphase's Forward Looking Sonar

Filter: a depthsounder feature that removes noise without reducing sensitivity

Fish reveal mode: Lowrance's reverse color feature; paints white pings on a dark background

FishTrack: Lowrance's feature that puts a digital depth next to a fish icon in "Fish ID" mode

Frequency: the number of vibrations per second in the transducer's crystal, measured in kiloHertz

FSTN: Film-compensated Super-Twisted Nematic; a liquid crystal screen with high pixel density; use less power

Gain: sensitivity; amplifies the returning sonar echoes; similar to volume control on a radio

GPS: Global Navigation System

GNSS: Global Navigation Satellite System

Grayline: Lowrance's depthsounder feature that depicts bottom type (sand, shell, gravel, mud, rock) by the thickness and darkness of the bottom signal painted on the screen, in about 10 shades of gray

HD-ID: Garmin's High Definition Identification depthsounder

HDI: Lowrance's Hybrid Dual Imaging, shows regular bottom images and picture-like images

HDS: Lowrance's High Definition System depthsounder

Hertz: one vibration per second

HPA: High Performance Addressing – a way to speed data display on a liquid crystal screen

Hybrid Touch: Raymarine's combination keypad/touch-screen feature

Hydrophone: synonym for depthsounder

Hyperscroll: Lowrance's ping-speed control

Ignition interference: power spikes from outboard motor or I/O engine can show up as noise on a depthsounder screen

Integrated display: allows you to display data on several depthsounders at once

Interference: two depthsounders operating on the same frequency can clutter each other's screens with noise

IP: Ingress Protection; this rating tells us how well the manufacturer protected the depthsounder from dirt, dust, and water intrusion; IP-X7 is good

Keel offset: calibrates the depthsounder's readout to allow for the transducer's depth in the water; add distance to show true bottom depth; subtract distance to show depth under keel

kHz: kiloHertz, 1,000 cycles per second; measures frequency of transducer crystal's vibrations

LCD: Liquid Crystal Display; new, transflective LCDs depend on sunlight reflecting off the screen to view an image; the brighter the sun, the brighter the image

LED: Light Emitting Diode

Locked SD card: protects card from over-writing; you cannot load new data onto the card when you slid the side tab away from the metal contacts end of the card

Look-ahead sonar: scans the water a few hundred feet ahead of the boat

MAP: Manufacturer's Advertised Price; retailer agrees to sue this price in ads; not necessarily the actual sales price

MBES: Multi-Beam Echo Sounder

MFD: Multi-Function Display

MMC: Multimedia Memory Card

Multibeam sonar: transducer sends down several sonar cones, each different in frequency or direction

Multicasting: allows an Ethernet system to send data from one device to many devices; all devices must operate on the same frequency

Multisensor: several sensors (depth, speed, temperature) in a single transducer housing

NIT: a unit that measures how bright a screen is; from the Latin, "Nitere," to shine

NMEA: National Marine Electronics Association; sets standards so electronic gadgets can talk to one another

Noise: unwanted signals on the screen; dots, dashes, squiggles, blobs, snow...

OLED: Organic Light Emitting Diode; an advanced screen that needs no backlight; thinner and lighter than an LCD; its high contrast ratio produces good images in low light conditions

ONIX: Hummingbird's multi-function display; has both a touch screen and touch keys

Overlay: numerical data in a screen window; examples: water temperature, boat speed, water depth, engine performance...

Paddlewheel: a spinning water wheel by the transducer that measures boat speed

PDP: Plasma Display Picture; a screen with very high resolution

Pan zoom: scroll the zoom feature up and down to search the water column

Peak to peak power: measures a depthsounder's maximum power, in watts

PAT: Interphase's Phased Array Technology; scans below boat, to sides, and ahead of boat

Phased array: a series of crystals in a transducer that fire in sequence to send sound signals

Piezoceramic element: transducer crystals with positive and negative charges

Ping speed: pulse rate; how frequently the depthsounder sends sonar signals into the water

Pixel: a Picture Element on the screen; each pixel turns on when electricity hits it

PDP: Plasma Display Picture; a screen with very high resolution

PPI: Pixels Per Inch; density of pixels on a square inch of screen

Power: the force of the outgoing sonar signal, measured in watts

Pulse rate: ping speed; pulse repetition rate; how frequently the depthsounder sends out sonar signals

Pulse width: the length of a sonar wave; depends on the amount of time the transducer is energized; the depthsounder fires electricity to the transducer every few microseconds; a low-frequency sonar has a longer pulse width than a high-frequency sonar

Quadra-Beam: Humminbird's term for 4 different sonar cones sent from one transducer

QVGA: Quarter Video Graphics Array (screen resolution)

Range: how deep the sonar signal penetrates the water column; you can choose a zone with upper and lower limits to display on the screen

Range scale: scale at right of screen that shows how far an object is from the transducer

Resolution: a depthsounder's ability to separate targets and paint them on the screen

RFI: Radio Frequency Interference; causes noise on depthsounder screen

Ring-down: the rate that a depthsounder sends signals into the water

RMS: Root Mean Squared – measures average sound power, in watts; about 1/8 of peak to peak power; the most honest way of expressing a depthsounder's power

SBAS: Satellite-Based Augmentation System; improves GPS accuracy; example: WASS

SCC: Surface Clarity Control; same as STC (Surface Turbulence Control); depthsounder's software that filters out surface clutter to produce a clearer, upper screen

Scroll speed: picture advance speed; rate that images move right to left across screen

SD card: Secure Digital memory card, SD-SC = Standard Capacity, SD-HC = High Capacity, SD-XC = Extended Capacity

Searchlight sonar: Furuno's term for scanning the water 360 degrees

Sensitivity: gain; a depthsounder's ability to detect and magnify echoes

Side imaging: side-scan sonar

Sidelobes: sound waves spill out to the sides of the main sonar beam; weak target echoes return from the sides

Side-scan: side imaging; structure-scan; a transducer's ability to look to each side of the boat

Side Vu: Garmin's sidescan imaging

Signal to noise ratio: sonar signal's power compared to the noise that results from that signal

Smooth scaling: Garmin's term for preserving screen history as depth changes

Soft key: a depthsounder button that can perform several functions

Solar max: Lowrance's bright screen

SONAR: SOund NAvigation Ranging; sound waves bounce off objects and return to transducer

Sounder: depthsounder; synonym for depthsounder

Spread spectrum: Garmin's term for broadband

Spotlight sonar: Lowrance's sidescan and look-ahead sonar

Squelch: depthsounder filters that remove noise and interference

Surface clutter: debris and air bubbles near the water's surface; these reflect sonar signals that show on the upper screen as noise

STC: Surface Turbulence Control; same as SCC (Surface Clarity Control); software that filters out surface clutter to produce a clearer upper screen

STC: Sensitivity Time Constant; depthsounder's software that filters out surface clutter by automatically lessening the gain in shallow water

Stop mode: feature that temporarily stops a depthsounder from receiving signals from the transducer

Streaking: a fish rapidly swimming away from the boat paints a slanted line on the screen

Structure Scan: side-scan; a Lowrance and Simrad depthsounder feature that scans down, ahead, and to each side, painting 3D images on the screen; fish often appear as blobs instead of arches

SwitchFire: Humminbird's dual-beam depthsounder; sidescan & downscan; switch between max mode (zoomed, much detail) and clean mode (auto-filters clutter out)

Target masking: blind zone; dead zone; sonar beam fails to detect fish under the shadow of an underwater ledge (blind zone)

TFT: Thin Film Transistor screen display; backlights the screen; as long as backlight exceeds sunlight image is OK

Thermocline: the vertical zone in the water column where temperature changes rapidly

Time variable gain: automatically vary the gain so a target echoes with the same strength no matter what the depth

Trackback: Lowrance's and Simrad's option to reverse scroll (left to right) to view past screens

Transducer: depthsounder's sound sender unit; contains one or more crystals that convert electrical impulses into sound waves, and back again

Transflective screen: a thin polymer sheet across the screen reflects intense sunlight, yet transmits a backlight in dim light

True echo: Furuno's CHIRP feature

Ultrascan: Interphase's forward-looking sonar

Ultrascroll: Garmin's rapid screen update system

Ultrasonic: sound waves higher than 20 kHz

Variable Pulse Modulation: when an electric trolling motor varies its speed by varying its electrical pulses, noise can leak into the transducer cable; this is called conductivity inference

VGA: Video Graphics Array; a way to provide good screen resolution

WAAS: Wide Area Augmentation System for GPS; improves accuracy to about plus or minus 15'

WASSP: Wide Angle Sonar Seabed Profiler; a 3D system that uses 2 transducers (one sends, one receives) to determine the depth and hardness of the seabed; uses a multibeam transducer (112 beams); used in Furuno's commercial depthsounders

WRMS: Watts Root Mean Squared; the average power a depthsounder uses

White edge: Furuno's thin white line along surface of sea bottom; allows us to see bottom-dwelling fish better

Whiteline: a Garmin, Standard Horizon, and SiTex depthsounder feature that distinguishes a soft bottom from a hard bottom by the thickness and shade of the band below the bottom line

WVGA: Wide Video Graphics Array (screen resolution)

XGA: Extended Graphics Array; a way to display data on a screen

Zero line: line at top of screen, at sea surface

Zoom: software that changes the screen's vertical scale to paint more or fewer pixels per foot of water depth

Quick Tips

Read the Water
- Calibrate the screen's depth readout.
- Look for a thermocline – a faint, consistent, flat line.
- Other horizontal lines: oxycline, halocline.
- Birds diving on bait may appear as slanted lines (their bubble trails).
- Weak dots deep – shrimp, prawns.
- Many small arches may be squid.
- Jellyfish can produce a false bottom.

Cut Clutter
- Surface Clarity Control/Surface Turbulence Control cuts clutter.
- Dial the gain up. Tolerate some screen clutter. Never sacrifice fish marks for a clean screen.
- The higher a sonar beam's frequency, the more detail it shows.
- To see bait and fish amid clutter, reverse the screen background color.
- Use "Noise suppression" sparingly.

Find More Fish
- Select a high-frequency sonar beam to see fish in shallow water.
- Choose a low-frequency sonar beam to find fish in deep water.
- See more fish. Turn "Fish ID" off.
- To get better fish arches, keep your boat moving.
- A half-arch marks a fish that swam at the edge of the cone.
- Screen streaks are fast-swimming fish.
- Turn "Fish alarm" on.
- Set range to "Manual." Set upper & lower limits to display only the zone you're fishing. Then zoom in.
- Set chart speed "Fast" for trolling, "Slow" for cruising.
- Scroll back to study a past screen.

Mark Bait
- Search for baitfish before you look for gamefish.
- Scan for bait with a wide cone angle. Then zoom in with a narrow cone angle.
- Bait that shows on the screen as a haystack is scared bait.

- The hotter the color of the center of a bait ball, the denser the ball.
- Bait that shows as a comet is moving bait.
- Adjust screen brightness/contrast to see bait in better detail.

Zero In

- Say, "Marking fish 50' away." Your screen shows how far a fish is from the transducer, not how deep the fish swims.
- The wider the cone angle, the more likely a fish will appear deeper than it really is.
- Dual frequency/split-screen: compare fish's arch in the wide cone to its arch in the narrow cone. If a better arch in wide, fish swims to the side.
- Guess a fish's size by its arch? No.
- To locate a fish in the cone, turn gain down. If fish disappears, it's probably swimming off to the side.
- Fish shows in wide-angle cone, disappears in narrow-angle cone: It's probably swimming off to the side.
- Estimate cone's width at a target depth, via a cone coverage table.
- In 3D mode, study the bottom for fish shadows.
- Zigzag over a steep slope to reveal fish in the blind zone.
- To spot fish in the blind zone, increase the sonar's ping rate.

Read the Bottom

- Set the range scale to "Auto" mode, or "Bottom track," to continuously paint the bottom on your screen.
- A soft bottom absorbs sound waves. Weak echo, cool colors.
- A hard bottom reflects sound waves. Strong echo, hot colors.
- A second bottom painted on the screen indicates a hard bottom.
- Monochrome screen: The lighter the gray, the denser the bottom.
- Depthsounder in auto mode: Study the screen's sensitivity (gain) bar. If the bar shortens, the bottom has grown harder.
- Gain controls how much the depthsounder amplifies echoes. Output power stays constant.
- The wider the band beneath the bottom line, the harder the bottom.
- Watch the screen's amplitude bar (far right side). The wider the bar, the harder the bottom directly under the boat.
- Compare digital depth with pictured depth. The greater the difference, the softer the bottom, or the steeper the bottom.

Mount the Transducer

- Transom mount – Sea trial the transducer on a movable board clamped to the transom before you drill holes in your boat.
- Transom mount – Place the transducer in between chines, close to boat's centerline, at least 12" (30 cm) away from a prop.
- Mount the transducer to avoid bubbles from strakes, ribs, steps, rivets, and through-hull fittings.
- Transducers require water-based, non-metallic, anti-fouling paint.
- Wash the face of your transducer with soap and water.

Lessen Screen Noise

- Most screen problems are transducer problems.
- Orient transducer face parallel to water surface, at cruising or trolling speed.
- At cruising speed, a higher-frequency sonar beam holds the bottom better.
- The higher a sonar beam's frequency, the less susceptible it is to noise.
- Two depthsounders on one boat: Run on different frequencies to prevent crosstalk.
- Run depthsounder and bow-mount trolling motor off separate batteries.
- Keep battery fully charged. If voltage drops, depthsounder power drops.
- Keep battery terminals and fuse holders clean.
- Noise from big engine? Run depthsounder off a different battery than the engine battery. Try a motorcycle battery.

Attend to Wires

- Wire your depthsounder directly to a battery.
- Route depthsounder wires far from other wires.
- Twist gadget wire pairs around each other to prevent magnetic fields.
- Ground all boat electrical gadgets.
- Use resistor spark plugs and plug covers, and noise-suppressing ignition wires.
- Depthsounder loses power in rough seas? Check for loose battery wires, loose fuses, loose cable plugs.

Index

Acknowledgements

"Thank you" to the following experts who reviewed text for accuracy and contributed ideas for improvement: Erin Boucher, and Paul Strawbridge, Airmar Technology, answered many questions about transducers and reviewed chapters 5 & 6. Lucie Fritz, PhD., proofread the manuscript for accuracy. Larry Till, Furuno U.S.A., reviewed chapters 5 & 9. Tom Zenanko, Vexilar, reviewed chapters 1, 2, 3, 4.

These people provided art that made this book possible: Del Bareither contributed photos. Erin Boucher & Paul Strawbridge, Airmar Technology, provided photos of transducers and diagrams of how they work. Phil Dawson, Legacy Lodge, BC, provided photos. Jim Edlund, media representative for Humminbird, provided photos of depthfinders and 3D screen shots. Captain Greg Ewart, Ventura Sportfishing Charters, donated a photo. Jeff Fortuna, Hobie Cat, furnished photos of canoe/kayak depthsounder setups and transducer installations. Lucie Fritz, Richland, WA, & Andrew Fritz, Renton, WA, donated photos. Ted Gartner, Garmin, provided photos of Garmin and Interphase depthsounders and screenshots. Andrew Golden, media representative for Navico brands (Lowrance, Northstar, Simrad) provided photos and art. Nelson Goodsell, Everett, WA, donated a photo. Debbie Hrea, Radarsonics, provided photos of transducers. Jaclyn Humphrey, Seattle, WA, donated a photo. Seth Hunter, JRC Marine Electronics, furnished images of depthsounders. Gabe Isham, Norcross Marine Products, provided images for Hawkeye depthfinders. Scott Johnson, Stern Saver Company, furnished photos from their website. Captain John Keiser, Salt Patrol, contributed photos. Jim McGowan, Raymarine, provided photos of depthfinders, screen shots, diagrams. Captain Tom Nelson, Salmon University, contributed photos. Nina Olson, Aqua-Vu, furnished product photos. Jennifer Piper, Airmar Technology, provided photos of transducers. Hans Rooker, Standard Horizon, provided photos of depthsounders. Steve Roth, Swanson Russell Agency, media representative for Minn Kota Motors (a Johnson Outdoors Company), provided images for trolling motors and transducer brackets. Terry Rudnick contributed photos. Allen Schnider, Sitex & Koden, contributed images of depthfinders. Larry Till, Furuno U.S.A., furnished photos and diagrams of depthsounders and transducers. Joe Tomelleri, Washington Dept. Fish & Wildlife, donated photos. Tom Wedgis, Faria Corporation, provided images of digital depthfinders. Terry Wiest, Steelhead University, donated photos. Dave Wiley, Orion Charters, Valdez, AK, contributed photos. Tom Zenanko, Vexilar, provided product photos.

These organizations provided photos & illustrations: California State University; Southwest Fisheries Science Center, NOAA, U.S. Dept. Commerce; Wikipedia Commons; NOVA Online; NGR Corp.; U.S. National Park Service; U.S. Fish & Wildlife Service; Northwest Salmon Derby Series; Cobia Boats; Mako Boats; Alaska Dept. Fish & Game; Alaska Seafood Marketing Institute; Greater Miami Convention & Visitors Bureau; Maryland Dept. Natural Resources; Echopilot; Hondex Corp.; Ohio Dept. Natural Resources; Cabela's; FloScan; World Wildlife Fund.

About the Author

Wayne Heinz fishes freshwater and saltwater throughout the Pacific Northwest. He logs each fishing trip—39 years' worth of weather, water conditions, catches, and depthsounder data, over 1,220 trips.

He mines these logs to write a monthly fishing column for *Pacific Nor'West Boating* and outdoor articles for 16 other magazines and newspapers—more than 100 stories over several decades.

Wayne has won 7 writing awards from the Northwest Outdoor Writers' Association. Other books by the author: *Fish On! How to Catch Salmon, Sturgeon, Lingcod, Rockfish and Halibut Along the Pacific Coast; Here's How to Catch Halibut; Here's How to Catch Flounder and Surfperch; Here's How to Catch Rockfish, Lingcod and Other Bottomfish.*

April through November, hail Wayne on the Columbia River, Puget Sound, or the Strait of Juan de Fuca, at the helm of his 25' sportfisher, *Merlin*, out of Cap Sante Marina, Anacortes, Washington. He runs four depthsounders on two boats, and has learned a bit about finding fish with sonar.

Meet Wayne in the winter during seminars at sports shows, boat shows, tackle shops, and chandleries.